Earth Science
Discovering the secrets of the earth

FOSSILS

Atlantic Europe Publishing

Atlantic Europe Publishing

First published in 2000 by
Atlantic Europe Publishing Company Ltd
Copyright © 2000
Atlantic Europe Publishing Company Ltd

Author
Brian Knapp, BSc, PhD

Art Director
Duncan McCrae, BSc

Editors
Mary Sanders, BSc and Gillian Gatehouse

Illustrations
David Woodroffe and Julian Baker

Designed and produced by
EARTHSCAPE EDITIONS

Reproduced in Malaysia by
Global Colour

Printed in Hong Kong by
Wing King Tong Company Ltd

Suggested cataloguing location
Knapp, Brian
    Earth Sciences set of 8 volumes
    Volume 3: *Fossils*
    1. Geology – Juvenile Literature
    2. Geography – Juvenile Literature
    550

ISBN 1 862140 43 X

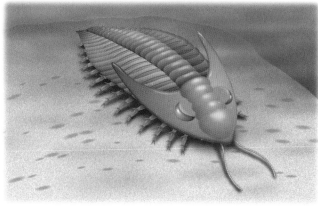

Acknowledgements
The publishers would like to thank the following for their kind help: *Anne and Ron Handy* for the photograph of *stromatolites*, *Charles Schotman* for the specimen of *Priscacara liops*, and *Oxford University Museum* for the specimen of *Ichthyosaurus quadriscissus*.

Contents

Chapter 1: The nature of fossils

A FOSSIL is any kind of remains, or trace of a former life. The word fossil comes from the Latin *fossilis*, meaning 'something dug out of the ground'.

The ancient Greeks were the first people to record a knowledge of fossils, but their ideas were lost for two thousand years. Fossils had to be re-discovered as former life forms. Leonardo da Vinci, for example, was one of the first to re-discover fossils in rocks and to see in them ancient sea creatures that had been buried before the muds and sands turned to stone.

Over the following centuries more and more was discovered about fossils, and this eventually led to their central role in our knowledge of what the earth was like in the past (see *Chapter 2*).

(Below) This fossil belemnite shows how careful we need to be about what is interpreted from the fossil we find. The diagram below shows that the fossil is only the hard part of a much larger animal.

(Below) Some rocks prove to be rich in past forms of life. These rocks contain ammonites.

(Right and below) A remarkable set of coincidences give rise to fossils and their discovery, as shown in the following sequence.

(a) Organisms die all the time. The cause may be old age, or they may have been killed by other organisms. Occasionally freak events, such as a storm or flood, may also cause large numbers to die at the same time and in the same place.

(b) Once dead, organisms normally decompose very quickly.

However, under special circumstances, decomposition can be slowed down. For example, a living thing might be buried rapidly in a landslide or flood, or it might come to rest on the bed of a lake in which there is little oxygen.

Under these special circumstances the organism can be preserved. Over time it can be buried by more deposits.

(c) Even the hard parts of a buried organism may decay, leaving only an imprint in the surrounding rock. Alternatively, the hard parts may be replaced by other minerals, a process known as **MINERALISATION**. If the rocks in which the fossils are buried are affected by heat or pressure, the minerals may change yet again, or the fossil may be destroyed.

(d) If the rocks come to the surface, they will be eroded. Fossils will be exposed for a while, because they are often harder than the layers of rocks that buried them. But, once exposed, it is only a chance encounter that results in the fossil being discovered before weathering or erosion destroys it.

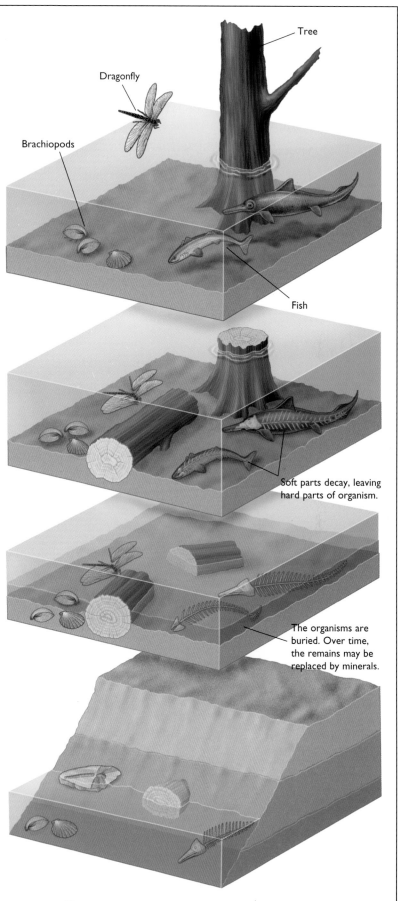

Tree

Dragonfly

Brachiopods

Fish

Soft parts decay, leaving hard parts of organism.

The organisms are buried. Over time, the remains may be replaced by minerals.

But fossils are not usually the undisturbed remains of creatures that have been buried. Many of the fossils that we see do not look very much like the plants or animals when they were alive. What we have to do is to learn to interpret the remains, and for this purpose we need to understand how fossilisation takes place.

Fossilisation

Living things are made mainly of water. This water bulks up the soft parts that make up most of an animal or plant while it is alive. Only the skeleton is hard. Skeletons come in two kinds: an outside covering, such as a shell (called an EXOSKELETON), or an inside skeleton such as is found in mammals and reptiles.

Most major groups of animals with external skeletons (INVERTEBRATES) have a skeleton or shell that is made of calcium carbonate, that is called a CALCAREOUS skeleton. Some other groups have shells of calcium phosphate. Bones of animals with internal skeletons (VERTEBRATES) are made of calcium phosphate.

When a living thing dies, the water leaves the body and the soft parts decay. The vast majority of living things decay and leave no trace. What we see preserved in rocks is a tiny fraction of the former life on earth.

With the soft parts decaying rapidly, it is far more common for only the hard parts to be preserved. Because the skeleton is often held together by soft tissue, the decay of soft tissue tends to allow the skeleton to fall apart. This is why it is more common to find parts of a skeleton – a single tooth, a leg bone, or a single shell – rather than a whole skeleton.

When any living thing is buried, the hard parts are protected from the wear and tear of the weather, waves, and currents, and have a better chance of being preserved. However, as more sediment builds up on top of the skeleton, it will be put under greater and greater pressure, so that finally

(Below) Trilobites are invertebrates and so have an external skeleton or shell. It is this that has been fossilised. The photo shows a cast. Nothing remains of the original skeleton.

(Below) This fossil shark's tooth is life size. As one of the hardest parts of the animal it belonged to, it is all that was left of a giant predator that would have been about 25m long. It is easier for us to interpret what the ancient shark would have looked like because sharks have changed relatively little in millions of years of evolution.

it may be squashed into a different shape.

What happens next depends not just on the pressure put on the skeleton, but also on the waters that slowly seep through as the rock forms. Hard parts, such as the shells of sea creatures, can remain unaltered, especially when the water is lime rich, as in the sediments that produce LIMESTONE rock.

(Below) Limestones often contain a wealth of skeletons because the limy waters preserved them. This is Silurian limestone and, although it is over 400 million years old, remains of many kinds of skeletons can be seen clearly.

If the water contains little lime, but is rich in other minerals, or if it is acid, the shells may dissolve away in the waters that seep through the rock. If the waters are acid, they can dissolve most skeletons. But if they are mineral rich, they may also bring new materials in solution that PRECIPITATE out in the exact place where the skeletons once existed. This process, called mineralisation, is possible for plants as well as for animals.

Some of the most impressive of all fossils produced by replacement of one mineral by another, are the giant trees in PETRIFIED FORESTS. The trees have had their bark and woody tissues entirely

(Below) The tree rings show up clearly in this cross-section of fossilised wood. This shows how mineralisation works at different rates in different tissues.

(Above) A fossil Triassic tree from the Petrified Forest National Park, Arizona, USA.

dissolved away and replaced by silica. They are now real stone, but the replacement is so perfect that the features of the original trees can still be easily made out.

Silica is just one of many materials that can replace the hard parts of a fossil. Pyrite is a yellow mineral that is commonly found in muds where the oxygen is poor. It can replace the shell of fossil sea-dwelling creatures with CASTS that are exact replicas of the original.

Even if there are no solutions replacing the dissolved hard parts, the rock may simply preserve the shape of the hard parts as MOULDS. Insects preserved in amber are usually moulds, although the insects in them are preserved in such minute detail that they seem to be the original organic materials.

A mould of a thin object, such as a leaf, is known as an IMPRINT.

(Below) The stages in making a cast or a mould of a fossil.

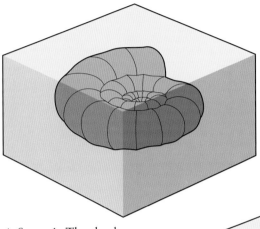

△ Stage 1. The dead animal is buried by sediment.

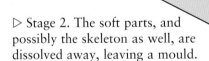

▷ Stage 2. The soft parts, and possibly the skeleton as well, are dissolved away, leaving a mould.

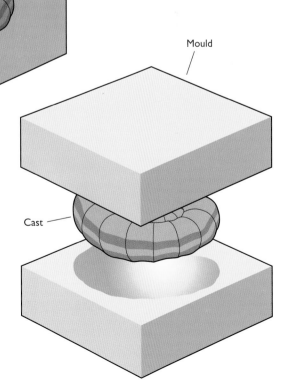

Mould

Cast

▷ Stage 3. Solutions passing through the sediment deposit minerals in the mould to produce a cast of the skeleton (and sometimes also the soft parts) of the original creature. Both mould and cast keep a record of the fossil and may be found in rocks.

(Left) A nodule in which fossil is preserved.

(Below) When the nodule is broken open, it reveals both cast and mould. On the left is the cast, on the right you can see part of the mould.

(Above) The 'insect' in this amber has, in fact, decomposed completely, and what you can see is a mould. Because an insect has an outer skeleton, the mould looks just like the outside of the original animal.

(Right) The leaves of this plant have broken down completely, leaving only a thin mould or imprint, which is highlighted in white by a powdery deposit that has filled the space.

In some cases, and especially with plants, some of the organic material is lost in the form of gases, while the carbon remains behind. This process, called DISTILLATION, leaves carbonised remains. Most fossil plants are of this kind.

Fossils may not be of actual living things at all. In some cases, trails of living things become preserved in the rocks. Dinosaur footprints and, more commonly, trails of insects are quite often found.

Where fossils are found

Some environments are more suited to the preservation of fossils than others. Molten rocks or those that have been subjected to great heat and pressure are the least productive fossil environments. Places where there have been fast-flowing currents are also poor in fossils. By contrast, environments where there were slow currents, and where there was little oxygen, are often very rich in fossils.

(Below) What was once the shell of this ammonite is now pyrite, a shiny yellow mineral.

(Below) The plant has left a trace with carbonised remains through distillation.

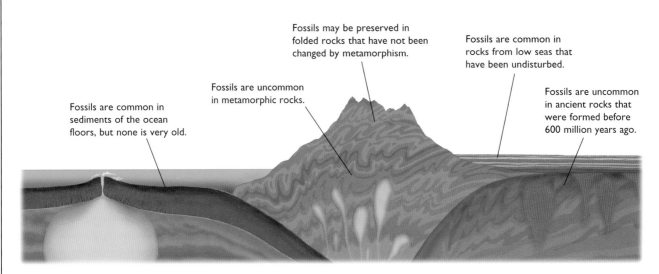

Fossils are common in sediments of the ocean floors, but none is very old.

Fossils are uncommon in metamorphic rocks.

Fossils may be preserved in folded rocks that have not been changed by metamorphism.

Fossils are common in rocks from low seas that have been undisturbed.

Fossils are uncommon in ancient rocks that were formed before 600 million years ago.

The importance of fossils

Fossils have provided the evidence for the evolution of life on earth. By comparing fossils with their living relatives, we can reconstruct ancient climates, environments, and geography.

Fossils are also important as markers for prospectors. Many fossils can be used as indicators of the places where natural resources are most likely to be found. Oil exploration is just one branch of prospecting that relies heavily on the fossil record for its discoveries.

Fossils and plate tectonics

PLATE TECTONICS is the study of the movement of the earth's crust through geological time. (For more information see the book *Plate Tectonics* in the *Earth Science* set.) Fossils have played a critical role in helping to find out the positions of the continents over time.

When scientists mapped the pattern of fossils over the earth, they felt that the distribution of the earliest fossils made no sense if the continents had always been where they are now. For example, fossils of identical species that could not swim were found on continents separated by tens of thousands of kilometres of ocean. Trying to solve this problem was one strand that led to the revolutionary idea that the continents might have moved during the history of the

(Above) Fossils are more frequent in certain geological conditions.

earth. In fact, fossils proved to be extremely useful in helping to reconstruct where the continents had been in the past. In this way it was possible to see that the continents had all been part of one giant landmass 300 million years ago, explaining why similar land-based animals could have lived on all the continents.

Fossils and geological time

The rocks contain a nearly complete record of the history of the earth. The information on which much of that record is based comes from fossils.

The rocks themselves may tell us, in a very general way, something about the environment when they were deposited. For example, the shape of the grains in a sandstone may hint that they formed in a desert or on a beach. But the living things that existed while the rock was being formed, are far more various and sensitive to environments than the grains in the

(Below) The distribution of a number of species of organism provided one of the early indicators of the past arrangement of the continents.

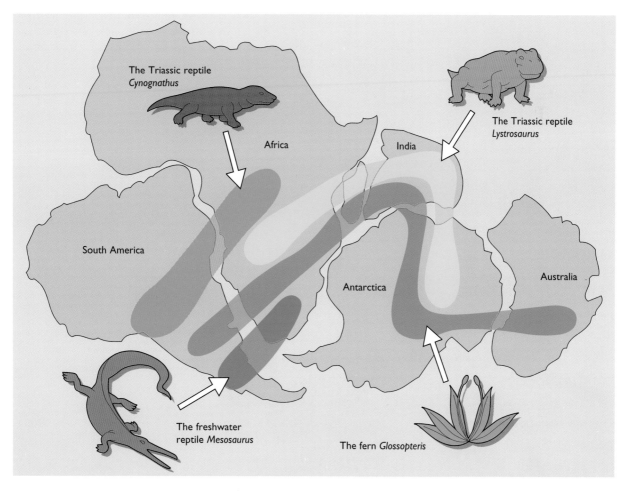

The Triassic reptile *Cynognathus*

The Triassic reptile *Lystrosaurus*

Africa

India

South America

Antarctica

Australia

The freshwater reptile *Mesosaurus*

The fern *Glossopteris*

rocks. For example, natural processes can give different SEDIMENTS that all form at the same time. Thus, a river will carry all kinds of sediment to the coast, but the coarser and heavier sands will be deposited to make a delta, while the finer and lighter muds will travel into the sea and be deposited as a layer of mud farther from the coast. These different sediments, all forming at the same time, are known as FACIES. They show that rocks of a similar age can be a sandstone (a sandy facies) in one place, while elsewhere they may form a SHALE (a muddy facies).

Fossils can be used to relate rocks over large areas, even when the rocks have very different textures. Thus, for example, a shale rock in one place might contain the same fossils as a sandstone or a limestone somewhere else.

There was also no doubt that fossils changed over

(Below) The same species of fossil can be found in different deposits because, despite their differences, the depositional process took place at the same time.

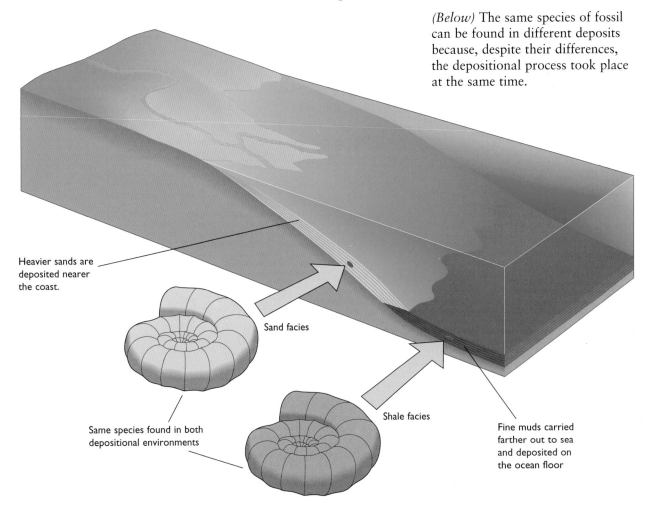

Heavier sands are deposited nearer the coast.

Sand facies

Same species found in both depositional environments

Shale facies

Fine muds carried farther out to sea and deposited on the ocean floor

time, with some species fading away and being replaced by others. Also, the fossil record bears the evidence of evolution, so that the evolution of fossils can be used to chart a continuous succession of former living things through time. This is the key to seeing that fossils can be used to build up a worldwide GEOLOGICAL TIME SCALE. (For more information on this topic see pages 50 to 59 and the book *Geological Time* in the *Earth Science* set.)

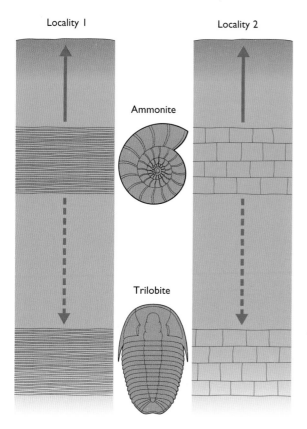

Locality 1

Locality 2

Ammonite

Trilobite

(Above) Ammonites are free swimming and can be found worldwide. They are good indicators of time, even when continents are separated.

(Above) Trilobites were bottom dwellers and found close to coasts. They could not cross large oceans. They are good indicators of the isolation of continents (or of their previous grouping).

(Above) This diagram shows the principle of how fossils can be used to make a geological record from rocks of different textures (facies). In the lower part of the diagram, an ancient form of life called a trilobite is found in both shale and limestone, indicating that they are both rocks of the same age. But, the trilobite is not found in the upper rocks because, by the time these rocks were laid down, it had become extinct. Here, a different fossil, an ammonite, is found in both shale and limestone rocks, and so it, too, can be used to relate rocks of different textures. Rocks are placed in their correct order in time, using fossils that have overlapping time ranges.

Chapter 2: Common fossils

Fossils are ancient forms of life, and so are classified in just the same way as modern forms of life.

Classification of living things moves from large groups that share basic similar features (KINGDOMS), down to much smaller groups containing only those members that can breed together.

The largest group is the kingdom. Animals are put in one kingdom, plants in another.

The kingdoms are divided into broad groups called PHYLA (singular phylum). A phylum may contain many thousands of species. The largest phylum, arthropoda, for example, contains all the insects, spiders, crustaceans, and trilobites.

Phyla are divided into CLASSES. Insects, spiders, crustaceans and trilobites all belong to different classes.

Classes are subdivided into ORDERS, then into FAMILIES, then into GENERA (singular genus), and finally into SPECIES. In this book, both genera and species names are shown in italics.

Most fossils can be identified relatively easily by genera, but usually only a specialist can identify an individual species. Thus, the distinctive colonial coral, which is often referred to as *Favosites*, is a genus within the phylum Coelenterata. The word genera leads to the expression 'generic name', which is the name most commonly used when describing fossils.

The number of common fossil genera is still large – over a thousand – but at least it is manageable after practice.

It is important to remember that only a few fossils remain to represent the innumerable living things that have inhabited this world. Furthermore, nine-tenths of fossils are those of marine life, because it is far easier for sea creatures to be buried and preserved in the calm, still, and oxygen-poor waters of an ocean than in the continuously disturbed environments on land.

(Below) Ammonites were very successful animals and are found through a significant section of geological time. They evolved quickly and developed distinctive shell patterns. Because they were also widespead, they make good fossils, which can be identified relatively easily (they can be used as index fossils). This makes ammonites very useful, particularly for the Mesozoic Era.

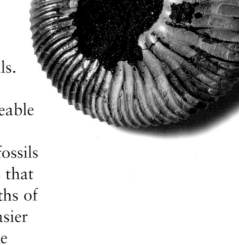

As a result, the vast majority of fossils are those of marine life. That is why most of the descriptions that will follow are of marine forms rather than of land-based life, such as insects (which are very fragile and rarely preserved) or dinosaurs, whose bones are rarely found and are even more rarely found together in a condition that allows them to be identified.

Here, then, are some of the more common levels of classification used. The most useful working description is the genus.

Broadest category		Phylum
		Class
Most useful name for describing fossils		Order
		Genus
		Species
Detailed category		

Examples:

Phylum	Mollusca
Class	Cephalopoda (subclass ammonoidea)
Order	Goniatitida
Genus	*Goniatites*
Species	*Goniatites globostriatus*

Phylum	Bryozoa
Class	Stenolaemata
Order	Cryptostomata
Genus	*Fenestella*
Species	*Fenestella plebeia*

Phylum	Cnidaria
Class	Anthozoa (subclass tabulata)
Order	Halysitida
Genus	*Halysites*
Species	*Halysites catenularius*

Corals

Corals (together with other animals such as jellyfish) belong to the phylum Coelenterata (meaning hollow gut). Only some Coelenterata secrete a hard skeleton, of which the most common is the coral.

Important groups include the tabulate corals (Tabulata), an extinct group found throughout the Palaeozoic Era. These were colonial corals made of many interlinked tubes called corallites. The corallites are braced with horizontal sheets called tabulae. *Favosites* (the honeycomb coral) is a common genus from the Silurian Period.

Solitary corals are much larger reef builders; they dominated the corals found in Upper Palaeozoic times, such as the Early Carboniferous Period. It is, therefore, called the Age of Corals.

Solitary corals begin from a basal plate, and the coral polyp then secretes its skeleton on top of this in the form of an outer wall and inner radial dividers called septa. An axial column occupies the centre of the structure. In section, these parts are easily identified (see opposite). There are two groups, the rugose corals (Rugosa), or wrinkled corals, which belong entirely to the Palaeozoic Era, and hexacorals, which are Mesozoic Era to recent. The rugose corals have four major septa, and the hexacorals have six.

Coral reefs and coral rocks do not consist entirely of corals, and corals do not always live in reefs, as you can see in the samples here.

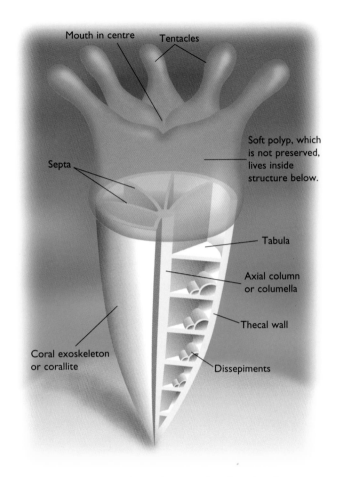

(Above) A coral polyp, showing hard and soft parts.

(Above) A fossil corallite.

(Below) A tabulate coral. Tabulate corals do not have septa and are always colonial.

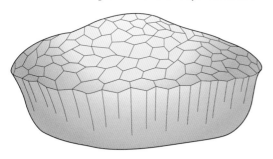

(Below) A rugose coral.

(Above and below) A modern hexacoral.

(Below) A coral in a red, muddy matrix.

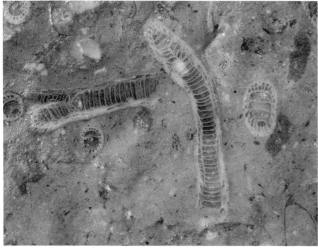

(Below) Carboniferous corals in longitudinal and cross-section.

(Below) Favosites, a Silurian tabulate coral.

A muddy matrix has filled in between the coral.

Recognising fossil corals

Corals can be found in a variety of rocks. Some corals form reefs, and others are solitary. Sometimes, corals are broken from the reefs they grow in and their fragments are scattered among the pieces of other shells. In many cases the corals are buried in a limy mud, so that they rarely form the whole of a rock, but are more usually scattered within it.

Fossil corals are most commonly found in limestones. Remember that not all limestones are white. They may be grey, if they have a large mud content, and they may be stained by river water washing over them.

You can distinguish tabulate corals from rugose corals by looking for the septa (the vertical divisions within the coral). Tabulate corals do not have septa, whereas rugose corals do. There are more major septa in hexacorals than in rugose corals.

(Left and above) You can often see fossils better if a surface has had time to be attacked by the weather. Many fossils then stand out of the matrix because they are harder and dissolve more slowly. This block of limestone is called a detrital limestone because it contains fragments (detritus) of shattered shells, corals and other fossil remains.

The inset shows a rugose coral that was spotted on the surface of the block. By turning the block around slightly, it can be aligned with the diagram on page 18 and the septa can then be identified.

This block also contains many other fossils.

Brachiopods

Brachiopods (Brachiopoda) are sea-living, double-shelled animals that first lived in Palaeozoic times. Some species of brachiopods still survive, although they are now quite rare.

Brachiopods were most common in the Palaeozoic Era, unlike bivalves (see page 29) which have become common mainly since the Mesozoic Era. Brachiopods have been used as index fossils for Jurassic and Cretaceous rocks.

The two shells, or valves, of a brachiopod are distinguished by being symmetrical (in a mollusc they are asymmetrical). The two valves are strongly convex, with one valve (the ventral) valve being much larger than the other. Some lived in shallow waters, attached to rocks by a stem-like structure called a pedicle. Others lived just below the surface of sandy beaches. Some had spines to help them remain stable enough to live on shallow, wave-washed beaches.

The earliest brachiopods are from the Cambrian Period, but they became much more common and varied in the Silurian Period (the Age of the Brachiopods).

(Below) The main characteristics of a brachiopod viewed from above (top) and the side (bottom).

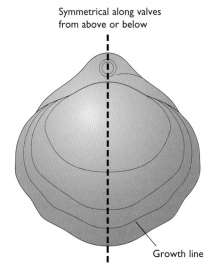

Symmetrical along valves from above or below

Growth line

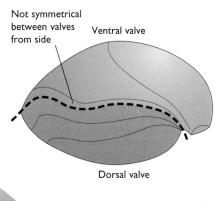

Not symmetrical between valves from side

Ventral valve

Dorsal valve

(Right) The hard parts (shown in red) are normally preserved in fossil brachiopods.

Dorsal valve

Muscles

Ventral valve

Pedicle for attachment to rock

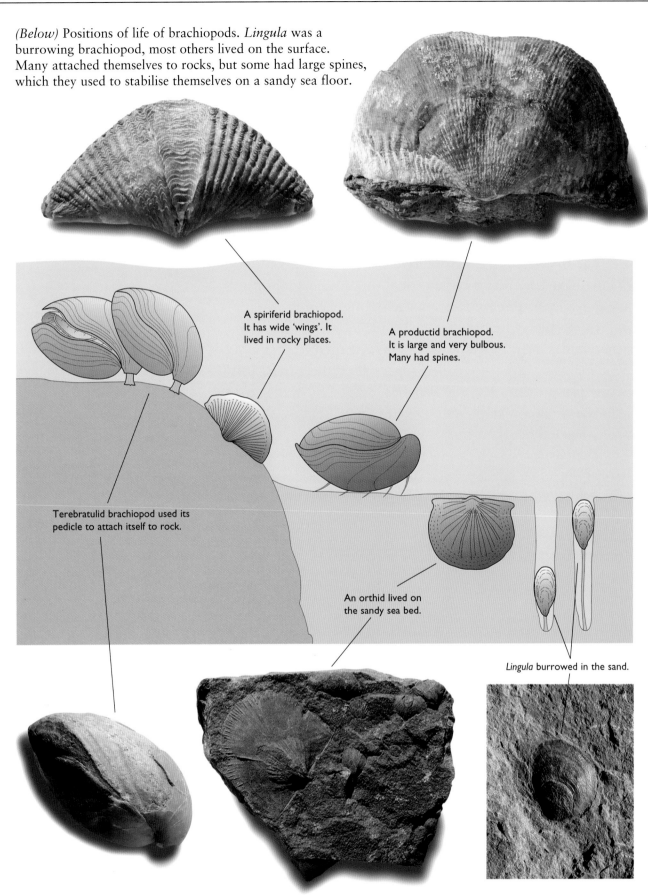

(Below) Positions of life of brachiopods. *Lingula* was a
burrowing brachiopod, most others lived on the surface.
Many attached themselves to rocks, but some had large spines,
which they used to stabilise themselves on a sandy sea floor.

A spiriferid brachiopod.
It has wide 'wings'. It
lived in rocky places.

A productid brachiopod.
It is large and very bulbous.
Many had spines.

Terebratulid brachiopod used its
pedicle to attach itself to rock.

An orthid lived on
the sandy sea bed.

Lingula burrowed in the sand.

Recognising brachiopods

Brachiopods are sea animals with two shells, or valves. Brachiopods can be confused with bivalves, but the way to distinguish them is to look at the line that goes through the valves. Brachiopods are symmetrical about this line, bivalves are generally not. Most brachiopods also have strongly bulbous valves. Brachiopods open and close the valves with two sets of muscles.

When they die, the withered muscles hold the valves shut, so that it is usual to find brachiopods as a complete shell of two connected valves. Bivalves, on the other hand, open up when the animal dies, and the valves become detached. It is, therefore, common to find clam valves separately, and uncommon to find them together.

(Below) Terebratulid brachiopod from above, the side, and below.

(Below) Rhynconellid brachiopod from above, from the side and slightly above, and from the back.

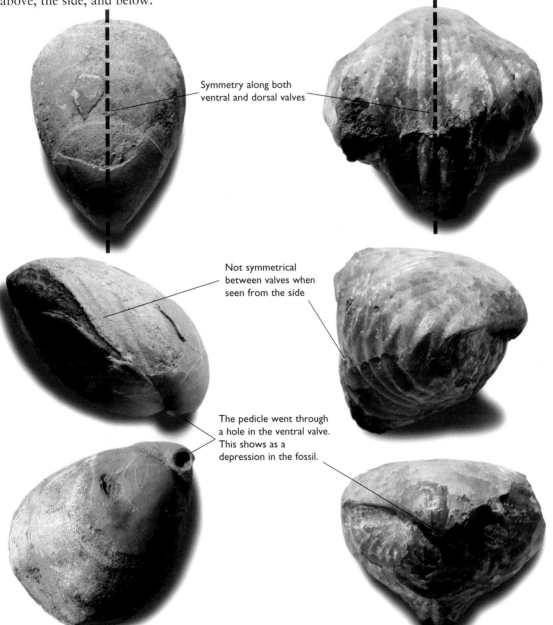

Symmetry along both ventral and dorsal valves

Not symmetrical between valves when seen from the side

The pedicle went through a hole in the ventral valve. This shows as a depression in the fossil.

Molluscs

Molluscs (Mollusca), which means soft bodied, is the name given to a wide range of classes of animal. They include the cephalopods (squids and ammonites), lamellibranchs (clams, bivalves) and the gastropods (snails).

Cephalopods

Cephalopods (Cephalopoda) are represented by the modern squid and nautilus, but they are important, geologically, for two ancestral versions, the belemnite and the ammonite. Ammonites were important from the Devonian to the Cretaceous periods, and belemnites from the Carboniferous to the Cretaceous periods.

These animals had a shell (internal in the case of the belemnite, or ancient squid), which is divided into a number of chambers. Air in the chambers allowed the animals to alter their buoyancy and so live at any depth they chose. They were able to move quickly through the water by squirting jets of water.

Belemnites

Belemnites were first found in the Carboniferous Period and were common in the Jurassic and Cretaceous periods. However, because ammonites are usually found in the same strata and ammonites are even easier to identify, belemnites have not been used as widely as might otherwise be the case. Belemnites are, however, used to date the Late Cretaceous because by this time most ammonites had become extinct.

Recognising belemnites

Belemnites are unusual in having their shell inside their bodies. The shell often breaks up into two pieces, with the more fragile guard being lost, and the more robust phragmacone surviving. The phragmacone contains chambers, separated by thin walls. In many cases the fossilisation process replaces the whole phragmacone with a single piece of silica. Then the phragmacone looks like a stone bullet. Just occasionally, especially in limestone, the phragmacone survives intact, and then a section through it shows curved lines, which represent the chamber walls.

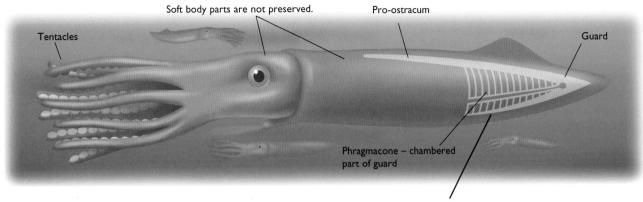

(Above and below) Only the hard parts (shown in pale brown on the diagram above) are what is preserved of belemnites.

(Below) Sections through phragmacone.

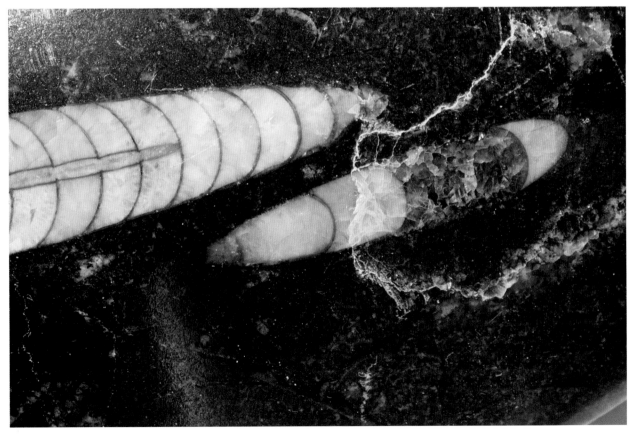

Ammonoids

Ammonoids are related to the modern nautilus. They lived between the Devonian and Cretaceous periods. Ammonoids lived in a chambered, coiled shell, the many chambers connected by a thin tube called a siphuncle. They were able to change the contents of the chambers to alter their buoyancy and existed at every level of the world's oceans. They were hunters, able to move quickly in search of prey.

Ammonoids developed a pattern of ribbed shells. The junction between the chamber walls and the outer shell is called the suture.

The earliest ammonoids are called goniatites (Devonian to Permian periods) and have a very simple suture pattern. They lived during the Palaeozoic Era. They were followed by ammonoids with a more complicated suture pattern, which were called ceratites (Devonian to Triassic periods). They were replaced by the ammonites during the Jurassic and Cretaceous periods. Ammonites developed a very complicated suture pattern that makes each species easy to identify.

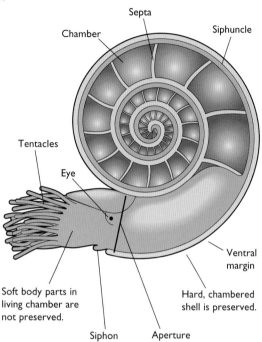

(Below) A section through an ammonite, showing chambers.

Septa

Chamber

Siphuncle

Tentacles

Eye

Soft body parts in living chamber are not preserved.

Siphon

Aperture

Ventral margin

Hard, chambered shell is preserved.

(Below) Ammonoids.

Swims by expelling water through siphon.

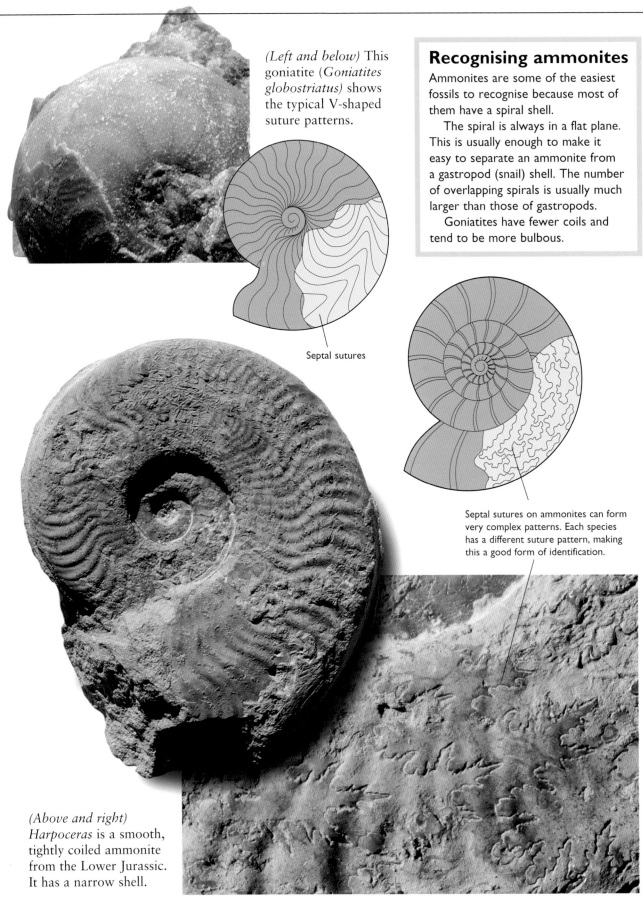

(Left and below) This goniatite (*Goniatites globostriatus*) shows the typical V-shaped suture patterns.

Recognising ammonites

Ammonites are some of the easiest fossils to recognise because most of them have a spiral shell.

The spiral is always in a flat plane. This is usually enough to make it easy to separate an ammonite from a gastropod (snail) shell. The number of overlapping spirals is usually much larger than those of gastropods.

Goniatites have fewer coils and tend to be more bulbous.

Septal sutures

Septal sutures on ammonites can form very complex patterns. Each species has a different suture pattern, making this a good form of identification.

(Above and right) *Harpoceras* is a smooth, tightly coiled ammonite from the Lower Jurassic. It has a narrow shell.

(Left) Dactylioceras ammonite from Upper Lias (Jurassic). *(Below)* The same genus when fossilised in pyrite and when extracted as a shale nodule.

(Left) An ammonite with a broad shell and wide opening.

(Below) A section through an ammonite, showing chambers and septa.

Bivalves

Bivalves (Bivalvia, Lamellibranchiata, Pelecypoda) are a common class of molluscs, which mainly thrive either attached to rocks near the shoreline, or buried in sand near the shore. They are also commonly known as clams. A few, such as *Pecten*, are able to move about by opening and shutting their valves quickly. Most attach themselves to one rock (for example, mussels), while a few use their foot to push themselves across the sand, or up and down in their burrow (e.g. razor shells).

Bivalves were rare in the Lower Palaeozoic Era, and even in the Carboniferous Period they were not common, although freshwater mussels are very important for relating various rocks formed on land.

Bivalves were much more common in the Mesozoic Era, when the number of species increased considerably. By the Tertiary Period, bivalves and gastropods were even more numerous and many beds are identified using them.

(Below) The main characteristics of a bivalve viewed from above (top) and the side (bottom).

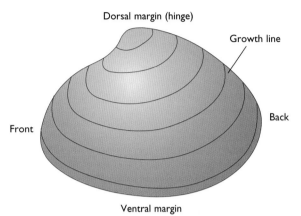

Dorsal margin (hinge)

Growth line

Front

Back

Ventral margin

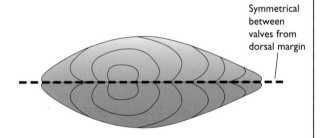

Symmetrical between valves from dorsal margin

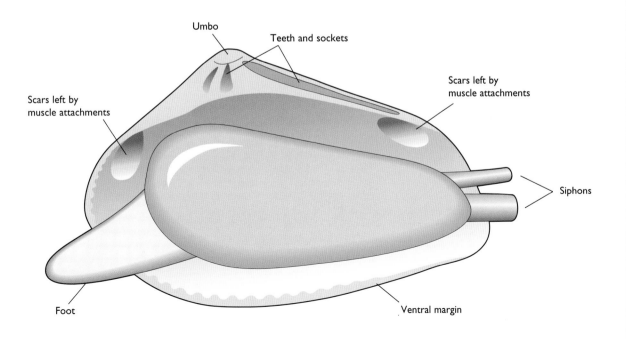

Umbo

Teeth and sockets

Scars left by muscle attachments

Scars left by muscle attachments

Siphons

Foot

Ventral margin

The soft parts of a typical bivalve are enclosed between two almost identical valves. The insides of the valves are usually pearly. The outsides of the valves have curved ridges. The edge farthest from the hinge, the ventral margin, is often crinkled (crenulate).

(Above) Complete bivalve found in mudstone, Jurassic.

(Below) Positions of life of bivalves.

Recognising fossil bivalves

Bivalves have two parts (valves) to their shell. The valves are fastened together with a fibre hinge that naturally causes the valves to spring apart. During their lives, the bivalves have a single muscle that keeps the valves closed. When they die, the muscle withers and the springy fibre hinge pops open, so that sea water can get into the valves, and they soon fall apart. For this reason it is rare to find both valves of a fossil bivalve (the example below is an exception).

Brachiopods are the only other two-valved fossil. When brachiopods die, the valves stay closed, and so both valves are found together. This is often the easiest way to distinguish a bivalve from a brachiopod. But, in addition, whereas the brachiopods valves are symmetrical about a line running from front to back, the bivalves are not. Instead, many bivalves have left and right valves that are mirror images.

(Below and right)
Nuculana

Symmetrical between valves from dorsal margin

Not symmetrical across both ventral and dorsal valves

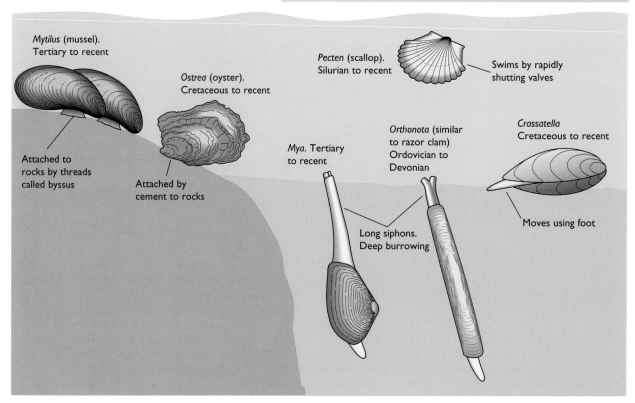

Mytilus (mussel). Tertiary to recent

Attached to rocks by threads called byssus

Ostrea (oyster). Cretaceous to recent

Attached by cement to rocks

Pecten (scallop). Silurian to recent

Swims by rapidly shutting valves

Mya. Tertiary to recent

Orthonota (similar to razor clam) Ordovician to Devonian

Long siphons. Deep burrowing

Crassatella Cretaceous to recent

Moves using foot

(Below) Inoceramus, Jurassic Period.

(Above and below) Gryphaea (Devil's toenail), Jurassic.

(Right) Ostrea (oyster), Jurassic, making a shelly limestone.

Gastropods

The gastropods (Gastropoda) include snails and whelks as well as limpets. Their large, sole-like foot is used to move them around. Snails are terrestrial, while limpets, whelks, and the like, live in shallow seas.

The shell is usually a conical, spiral shape. It has no divisions (which distinguishes it from ammonites). Some gastropods have coiled shells, others have straight shells. Coiled gastropods are very varied and are used for identifying Tertiary rocks.

Gastropods first developed in Palaeozoic times, but remained uncommon throughout this era and even throughout much of the Mesozoic Era. They are very distinctive in some beds, however, and very common in, for example, the Jurassic 'marble rocks'. Gastropods were most abundant in the Tertiary Period.

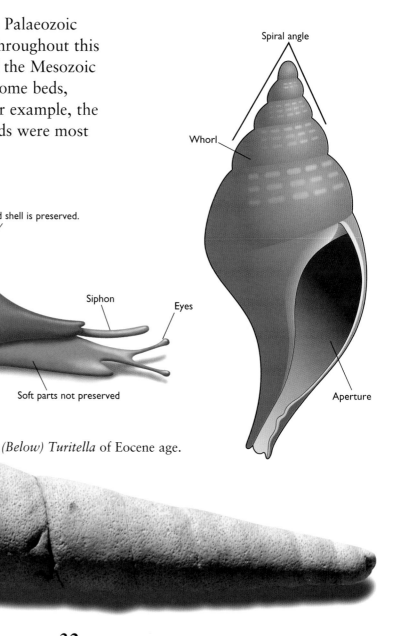

Recognising gastropods

Gastropods have a single shell. Many have a spiral whorl, making them snail-like to look at. However, many others do not have a whorled shape. The only other coiled fossil is an ammonite. Whorled gastropods have a single whorl with no walls between chambers, whereas ammonites have a spiral shell with many chambers. This is the easiest way to distinguish gastropods from ammonites.

Spiral angle

Whorl

Aperture

Hard shell is preserved.

Siphon

Eyes

Operculum

Foot

Soft parts not preserved

(Below) *Turitella* of Eocene age.

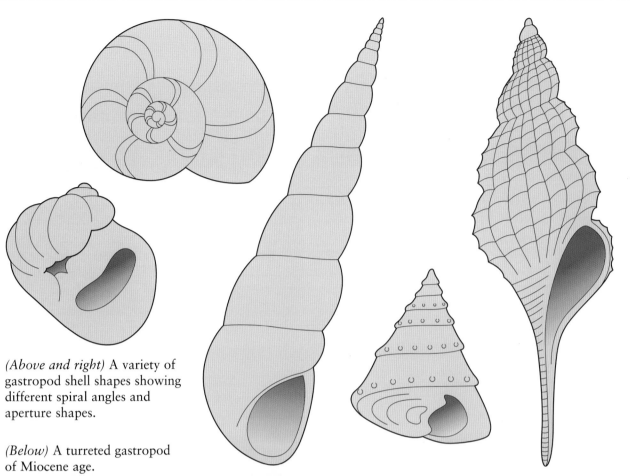

(Above and right) A variety of gastropod shell shapes showing different spiral angles and aperture shapes.

(Below) A turreted gastropod of Miocene age.

Echinoderms

Echinoderm (Echinodermata) means spiny-skinned. Echinoderms include many ancient forms of life that have survived to the present day, such as crinoids and sea urchins (echinoids).

Crinoids

Crinoids, which are animals although they are often called sea lilies, are among the oldest echinoderms. The main body, or calyx, is supported on a stem made of many ossicles. In many cases, the bottom of the stem is anchored to the sea bed.

Crinoids, like other echinoids, are noted for their five-fold symmetry. Five arms are attached to the cap, again made of ossicles. The arms are covered in tiny hairs (called cilia)

(Below) Ossicles from the stem of a crinoid.

(Below) Crinoid stems, calyx and arms preserved in a Silurian ironstone.

that beat in rhythm to carry food from the water down to the mouth in the cap.

Crinoids range from the Ordovician Period to modern times, but they were most common and geologically most important in the Upper Palaeozoic. Beds of limestone are often dominated by crinoid fragments of this age, when 'forests' of crinoids must have covered large parts of the sea bed. The Silurian has been called the Age of Crinoids.

Recognising crinoids

Crinoids grow to a wide variety of sizes. The stems commonly break up into the segments, called ossicles, and these disc-shaped pieces are scattered in many rocks. Each ossicle has a central hole.

It is much less common to find a head (calyx) and even rarer to find arms.

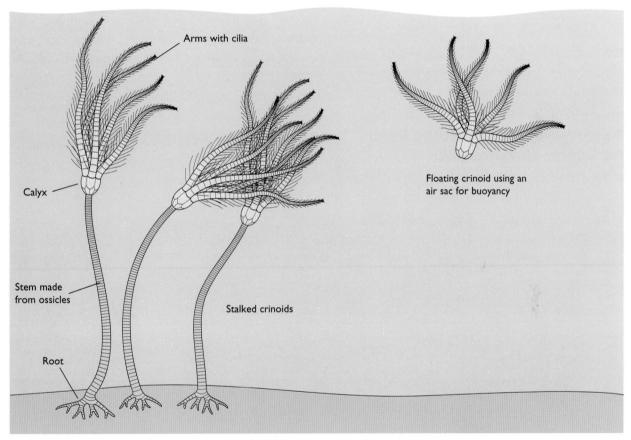

Arms with cilia

Calyx

Stem made from ossicles

Root

Stalked crinoids

Floating crinoid using an air sac for buoyancy

Radial plate

(Left) The calyx of a crinoid from the side, showing the plates with five-fold symmetry and connection to the stem.

(Right) The same calyx from above, showing the central mouth and five stubs where arms would have been attached.

Echinoids

Echinoids, or sea urchins, have five-fold symmetry like other echinoderms, in this case made from five plates that form the bulbous shell. When they are alive, a skin runs over their shells and the numerous spines are attached to it. When echinoids die, the spines fall away from the main shell, so that shells, often look more like knobbly balls.

Many echinoids move across the sea-bed using a combination of their tube feet and their spines. Some echinoids (for example, *Micraster* and *Hemiaster*) burrow in sand, and in these cases their spines are adapted and become almost hair-like.

Echinoids were uncommon in Palaeozoic rocks, but they are frequently found in both Mesozoic and Cenozoic era rocks. Echinoids are used as index fossils in Cretaceous rocks.

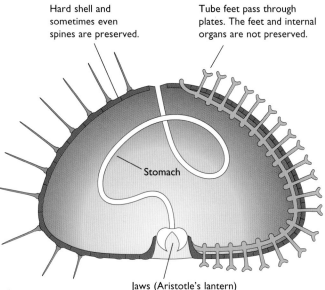

(Below) Cross-section through a regular echinoid.

Hard shell and sometimes even spines are preserved.

Tube feet pass through plates. The feet and internal organs are not preserved.

Stomach

Jaws (Aristotle's lantern)

(Below) The habitats for a some echinoids and starfish.

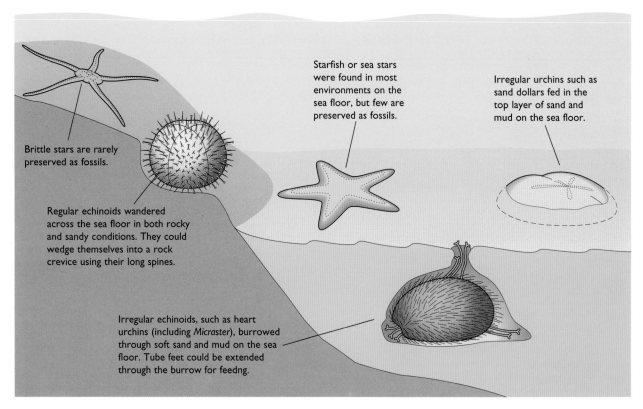

Starfish or sea stars were found in most environments on the sea floor, but few are preserved as fossils.

Irregular urchins such as sand dollars fed in the top layer of sand and mud on the sea floor.

Brittle stars are rarely preserved as fossils.

Regular echinoids wandered across the sea floor in both rocky and sandy conditions. They could wedge themselves into a rock crevice using their long spines.

Irregular echinoids, such as heart urchins (including *Micraster*), burrowed through soft sand and mud on the sea floor. Tube feet could be extended through the burrow for feedng.

(Left) The mouth parts on the underside of a modern echinoid.

(Right) The 'shell' of a modern bulbous, rock-dwelling, regular echinoid as seen from above. The many bumps show where the slender spines fitted.

Recognising echinoids

Echinoids are mainly bulbous fossils. It is not always possible to find evidence of the five plates or the spines. However, their shape makes it difficult to mistake them for any other fossil.

You may also find spines separately. They are thin rods of material and are not as readily identified.

(Left) Modern, flat, irregular echinoid, known as a sand dollar. Its flat shape gives it stability on the sand.

(Above) Hemicidaris from above, showing the many ball-shaped protrusions on which the spines rotated. It is a Jurassic echinoid that lived wedged in the rocks.

(Right) Cidaris from below. The large sediment-filled opening is where the jaws were located. It is a Jurassic echinoid that lived wedged in the rocks.

(Above) Micraster and *Hemiaster* are two common heart-shaped Cretaceous echinoids that had hairy spines, and which burrowed in the sand. The heart-shaped shell would have a been a kind of streamlining to help the animals bulldoze their way through the sand. Notice the marking on the top of the fossil, showing the five plates.

Arthropods

Arthropods (Arthropoda – whose name means joint footed) make up about three-quarters of all known invertebrates.

All arthropods are symmetrical about a line down the centres of their bodies. The body is also divided into segments, and the segments each bear pairs of jointed limbs, wings or jaws. The soft parts are protected by the 'shell' (exoskeleton), which is on the upper (dorsal) side of the animal. Because the arthropods are invertebrates, their bones cannot grow steadily, but must be shed and re-grown periodically. The shedding of shells results in large amounts of fossil material.

The arthropods are divided into insects, spiders, crustaceans (crabs, etc.), centipedes and millipedes, and trilobites.

Many insects and spiders have delicate bodies that are not well preserved as fossils except in special circumstances, such as when they are found in amber. Fossils from crustaceans are more common. Trilobite remains are also commonly preserved.

(Above) Tertiary insect in amber.

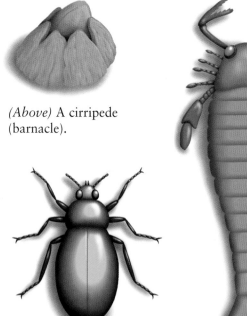

(Above) A cirripede (barnacle).

(Above) A eurypterid.

(Above) Limulus, the king crab.

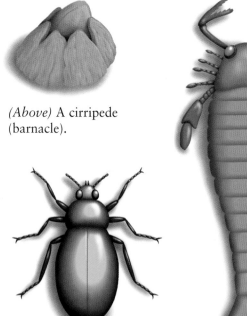

(Above) A Carboniferous beetle.

Trilobites

Trilobites (meaning three sections) are an extinct form of arthropod, but they have been very important in geological studies.

Trilobites could walk on the sea-bed or swim in shallow water. They were scavengers that regularly moulted their skeleton.

The first trilobites were found in Lower Cambrian rocks, and so they are among the earliest of fossils. The Cambrian Period has been called the Age of Trilobites. They show considerable variation in shape and size. Some grew to be over half a metre long.

Trilobites became most numerous and most varied in the Ordovician Period, and then began to decline, so, although they were still important in the Silurian Period, they were rare by the Carboniferous Period, and became extinct in Permian times.

(Below) Possible reconstruction of a trilobite.

Recognising trilobites

The oval shapes of trilobites are quite distinctive. They also have many lines across them. There are no lines on the head, and the head is more bulbous than the tail.

Recognising parts of trilobites and those that have been squashed is more difficult. It is quite common to find tails, but the lines running across the tail section should be easy to spot.

It is also common for some trilobites to be curled up, so do not expect to always find them as flat shapes.

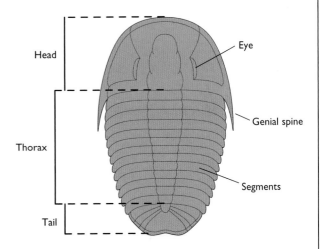

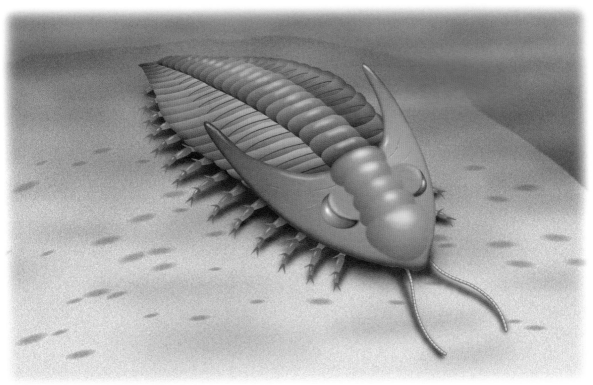

(Left) Paradoxides, a
Cambrian trilobite,
mould. *(Below)* A cast
of the same specimen.

(Above) Ogyginus,
Ordovician.

(Above and below)
Phacops, Devonian.

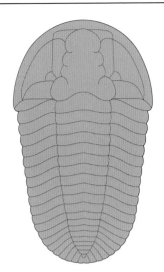

(Above and right)
Calymene, Silurian.

(Below) *Stapellella*, Ordovician.

(Left and below) *Elrathia*, Cambrian.

Vertebrates

The vertebrate part of the animal kingdom (Vertebrata) contains fish, amphibians, reptiles, birds, mammals and graptolites.

Vertebrate fossils are far less common than invertebrate fossils, partly because vertebrates are far outnumbered by invertebrates, and partly because the vertebrae fall apart when a vertebrate dies, so that good, whole specimens are extremely rare. Also, most vertebrate remains are difficult to identify without knowledge.

Graptolites

Graptolites are some of the most unusual and also some of the most important vertebrates of the Lower Palaeozoic times. As fossils, they are found either as white films or as solid shapes made of pyrite. Because people thought they looked like ancient writing, they were given the name graptolites, meaning stone writing.

Graptolites are made of either one, two, four, or many, branches, known as stipes. Along each stipe (a kind of backbone) are many small cups. In each cup was a food-gathering organ.

The earliest graptolites, which tend to be colonial and consist of numerous branches, are found in rocks of Cambrian age. They are thought to have been floating colonies, held up by some form of air bag. The less branched forms appeared in the Ordovician Period, and rapid evolution made them especially useful as index fossils for the Lower Palaeozoic Era. Because they were free floating, they were able to move about through all of the seas, and so they are very useful for comparing Lower Palaeozoic rocks around the world.

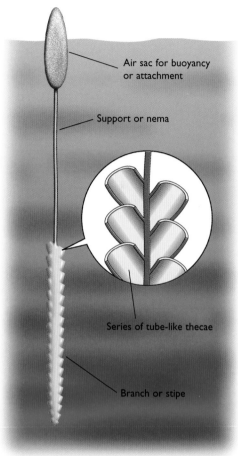

(Below) The parts of a graptolite.

Air sac for buoyancy or attachment

Support or nema

Series of tube-like thecae

Branch or stipe

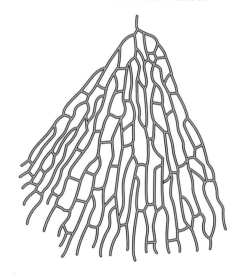

(Below) Dictyonema, a primitive dendroid graptolite from the Cambrian Period.

Recognising graptolites

Graptolites are mainly found as thin films or rods made of pyrite. They are normally found by breaking open sheets of shale. Because they are impressions and not usually solid objects, and because they are often small, they can easily be missed. Most graptolites are spotted by imagining their shape to be long, thin, saw-like blades.

(Left and above) Didymograptus, an Ordovician graptolite, recognisable for having two stipes.

Ordovician   ## Silurian

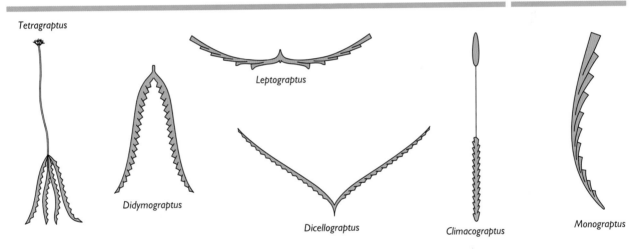

Tetragraptus

Didymograptus

Leptograptus

Dicellograptus

Climacograptus

Monograptus

(Above) Graptolites evolved to have fewer stipes.

(Below) Films of Monograptus.

(Above) A pyritised rod of Monograptus, a single-stiped graptolite from the Silurian.

Fish

Sharks and rays are some of the oldest fish: they are groups that have shown remarkably little evolutionary change. Sharks of the Upper Devonian age are hard to distinguish from modern sharks.

Normally, only isolated teeth are found. Because they have evolved so little, they are not used to date rocks.

Bony fish have a long history. Many of them had thick, heavy scales, looking like a kind of armour. They are first found in the Devonian Period, and, although modern fish are less armoured, they survive to the present day in examples like the sturgeon.

(Above) Tertiary fish preserved in siltstone.

(Below) Bony fish can leave complete skeletons. *Dunkleosteus* was a predatory bony fish that could grow to 10 metres. It lived during the Devonian Period.

(Above and right) The cartilage that makes up the skeleton of cartilaginous fish, such as sharks, is rarely preserved in fossils. Sharks' teeth, however, remain as evidence of their presence.

(Above) The skeletons of bony fish can produce beautiful fossils, such as this fossil of the freshwater fish *Priscacara liops*. This specimen is 53 million years old, placing it in the Tertiary Period.

Reptiles

Reptiles developed from one branch of the amphibians in Permian times. The major change was that they laid eggs that were protected by a shell. This allowed them to live entirely on land.

The early Permian and Triassic reptiles were quite small. Some were hunters, others grazed and browsed the vegetation. But, by the Jurassic and Cretaceous periods, evolutionary trends had produced an extraordinary variety of reptiles, some still small, but others of gigantic size. Thus, this time is called the Age of the Reptiles.

The dinosaurs (meaning terrible lizards) are a very varied group and include the largest land-based hunters of all times. The most massive of these hunters, *Tyrannosaurus rex*, weighed up to 8 tonnes and was over 12 metres long. The plant eaters were even bigger, the swamp-dwelling *Diplodocus* weighed up to 50 tonnes and could be 25 metres long.

Swimming reptiles included the ichthyosaurs, whose streamlined bodies made them look like porpoises, except that they carried fearful rows of teeth in their jaws. Another marine group was the plesiosaurs, adapted with long necks and paddle-like feet. There were also flying reptiles, the pterosaurs, with membranes between their limbs to act as wings.

(Above and below) Vertebrae from dinosaurs, showing the dished discs with knobbly protrusions.

(Above) A complete skeleton of an ichthyosaur (*Ichthyosaurus quadriscissus*). Great skill was needed to pare away the sediment that surrounded it.

The modern survivors of all of these include the crocodile and the turtle. Reptiles, however, are not used to date rocks, and it is extremely rare for complete skeletons to be found. Most finds of reptiles are simply of individual vertebrae, like the ones shown here.

In some special locations they can be seen in large numbers, for example, in Dinosaur National Monument, Colorado and Utah, USA.

Recognising dinosaurs and other vertebrates

Dinosaur remains are not common. When they die, the bones usually become separated. The most you can expect to find are the vertebrae and teeth. The vertebrae are usually knobbly, dished discs that can measure many centimetres, or even tens of centimetres across.

(Left) A bone bed full of dinosaur remains.

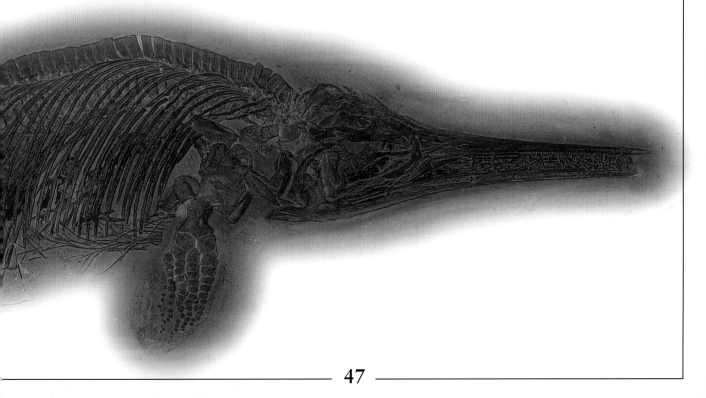

Plants

Some of the world's most important plants are the tiny, single-celled organisms called algae. They are the basis of many food chains, and they also secrete a hard, limy skeleton. Moreover, they occur in vast numbers. For this reason, they have become important rock builders through much of geological time. Many coral reefs are made up mainly of algae. The earliest living things, the stromatolites, are made of mats of algae. The calcified remains of tiny algae, called coccoliths, make up chalk rock.

Algae absorb nourishment through their surfaces. More developed (vascular) plants can extract nourishment from water and soil. Some of the oldest plants, the pteridophytes (horsetails, ferns), reproduced by spores; later, seeds became more common.

Pteriodophytes dominated the land in the Upper Palaeozoic Era. Seed-bearing plants were already important by the Upper Carboniferous Epoch.

Plants do not provide the easiest way of dating rocks because species are hard to identify from partial remains.

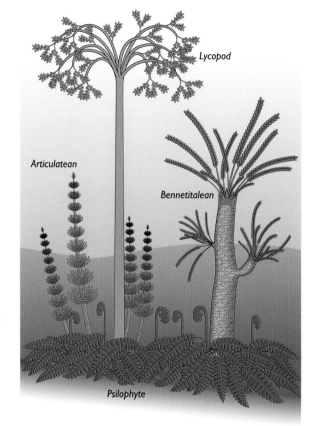

(Above) Forest plants from the Carboniferous Period.

(Left and above) Petrified wood.

An angiosperm (flowering plant) from the Tertiary Period

(Below) Leaf shapes of some common seed ferns from the Carboniferous Period.

Pectoperis

Annularia

Sphenopteris

Sphenophyllum

Alethopteris

Neuropteris

Carboniferous seed-fern *Neuropteris*

49

Chapter 3: Fossils and the geological record

The most important ways in which fossils can be helpful to earth science is through their ability to indicate both the passage of time and changes in environments throughout the world.

Divisions of the geological record

All of geological time is divided into two EONS: the PRECAMBRIAN Eon, followed by the PHANEROZOIC Eon. The Precambrian Eon is the time from the formation of the earth until evolution had progressed sufficiently to produce animals with hard parts that could commonly be preserved as fossils. This time makes up 88% of the entire history of the earth. The Phanerozoic Eon begins about 600 million years ago and continues to the present day.

Because the Precambrian Era contains little evidence of life, it cannot readily be divided up using fossils. However, the Phanerozoic is divided into three ERAS: the PALAEOZOIC (which means the time of early life forms), the MESOZOIC (time of middle life forms), and CENOZOIC (time of later life forms).

In turn, the eras are subdivided into PERIODS, which are of most practical use. Thus, we speak of the Palaeozoic Era being divided into Cambrian, Ordovician, and other periods. Each of the periods is further divided into EPOCHS. Epochs are either early, middle, or late, except for the Tertiary, where they are given individual names such as Eocene and Miocene. The rocks belonging to a period are called SYSTEMS, and the rocks belonging to an epoch are called SERIES. So, the Cambrian Period contains the Cambrian System rocks, and the Early Cambrian (Epoch) contains the Lower Cambrian Series rocks.

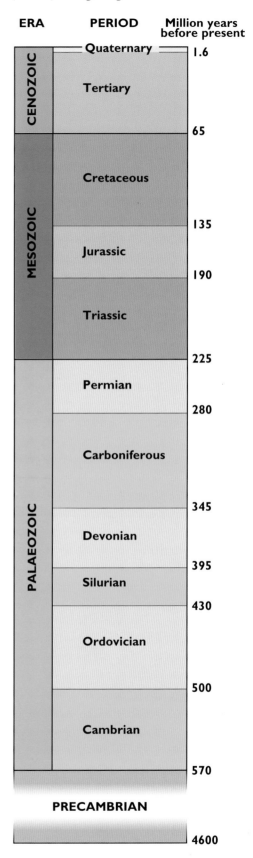

(Below) The geological time scale.

ERA	PERIOD	Million years before present
CENOZOIC	Quaternary	1.6
CENOZOIC	Tertiary	65
MESOZOIC	Cretaceous	135
MESOZOIC	Jurassic	190
MESOZOIC	Triassic	225
PALAEOZOIC	Permian	280
PALAEOZOIC	Carboniferous	345
PALAEOZOIC	Devonian	395
PALAEOZOIC	Silurian	430
PALAEOZOIC	Ordovician	500
PALAEOZOIC	Cambrian	570
	PRECAMBRIAN	4600

Fossils of Precambrian time

570 million to 1 billion years ago	Sponges, jellyfish, and primitive arthropods (trilobites)
2 billion to 3 billion years ago	First stromatolites
3 billion to 3.4 billion years ago	First primitive cells (algae)
4.6 billion years ago	Earth formed

The first life found in rocks is dated at 3.4 billion years ago, a remarkably short time after the earth first came into existence. The rocks containing the world's earliest known fossils are in South Africa; in them, microscopic life forms can be seen that are similar in shape to modern bacteria and blue-green algae.

A much more substantial form of life began to grow some 3 billion years ago, when large colonies of blue-green algae built themselves into large mats called stromatolites. At the same time, the algae began to secrete calcium carbonate, thus producing the world's first fossils.

It took nearly 2 billion years for more sophisticated life forms to evolve. The first evidence we have of them is from rocks 1.4 billion years old. They were early marine plants, able to get the energy they needed by using sunlight. As they used sunlight in the process of photosynthesis, they gave out oxygen, thus beginning a long process of change in the atmosphere that would eventually lead to the evolution of animals on land.

Evolution seems to have been much more rapid after the early plants developed. By 1 billion years ago there is evidence of worms, but the fossil record is so poor for this ancient time that little more is known.

It seems reasonably certain that evolution

(Below) Mats of algae that formed stromatolites were the first colonial form of life. They began in the Precambrian and are still growing today. This makes them one of the most successful forms of life on earth.

continued apace, but that all of the creatures were soft bodied, so that their remains are very rarely preserved. The first evidence of more developed life (including sponges, jellyfish, and insects) comes from Australian rocks dated at about 680 million years ago, and by then there are at least four separate major groups of life, or phyla.

The Palaeozoic Era

The Cambrian Period

500 million years ago	Mass extinction: trilobites greatly reduced
570 million years ago	Stromatolites abundant First gastropods, molluscs, crinoids, trilobites, brachiopods, graptolites

The Cambrian Period marks the sudden change, some time after 570 million years ago, to evolution that included hard shells and other forms of skeleton. Of this period, the most important guide fossils are the trilobites. They occurred all over the earth and evolved quite rapidly, so that their evolution can be used to trace the divisions of Lower, Middle and Upper Cambrian Epochs.

Although trilobites made up, perhaps, three-quarters of all known species, there were many other living things at this time. Among the most common remains are brachiopods and tiny fragments of sponges, known as spicules. Less common, but nonetheless present, are the molluscs and gastropods, as well as small cephalopods. Echinoderms had evolved, but were rare. Corals do not occur in the Cambrian Period. There was no life on land.

At the end of the Cambrian Period an unknown event happened that caused a large number of families to die out. It is called a MASS EXTINCTION. It made nearly half of all trilobite families perish.

(Below) Cambrian trilobite: *Paradoxides.*

(Below) Cambrian trilobite: *Lingula.*

(Below) Cambrian trilobites: *Elrathria* (larger specimen), *Ptychagnostus* (smaller specimen).

The Ordovician Period

430 million years ago	Mass extinction: trilobites, crinoids and brachiopods greatly reduced in numbers
430 to 500 million years ago	Gastropods, crinoids, trilobites, brachiopods, graptolites increase in numbers again. First corals and vertebrates

Brachiopods became a more important form of life; echinoderms were also more important, especially crinoids. In the Ordovician Period they were still small. Gastropods became larger and more common, as did molluscs, although their number was small. Crinoids continued to thrive.

Corals made their first appearance in the Ordovician Period, first as tabulate forms, then, by mid-Ordovician, as rugose forms as well. Graptolites had become abundant, and the fact that they were free floating and so found everywhere makes them useful index fossils. The first vertebrates also lived in the Ordovician Period. They were the ancestors of fishes and all other vertebrates.

At the end of the Ordovician Period there was a second global catastrophe and mass extinction when about a quarter of all families died. The trilobites fared worse than most other families. Large numbers of brachiopods and echinoids also suffered.

(Above) Ordovician trilobite: *Ogygenus.*

(Below) Ordovician graptolite: *Didymograptus.*

The Silurian Period

395 million to 430 million years ago	Corals and crinoids abundant. First land plants, growth in arthropods, fish with jaws

The Silurian Period is short, and no new major groups of organisms evolved. Corals became more numerous and large reefs formed. Trilobites and graptolites still survived, but in restricted numbers. On the other hand, scorpion-like arthropods grew to be enormous, and some example fossils show they reached 3 metres in length, the largest arthropods ever to be on earth. The first fish with jaws developed but were rare. The first plants appeared on land. At this time, however, the land plants had no leaves.

(Above) Silurian graptolite: *Monograptus.*

The Devonian Period

345 million to 395 million years ago	Mass extinction: corals, ammonoids, trilobites, fish greatly reduced. Land plants with seeds, molluscs, sponges, corals, brachiopods abundant. First ammonoids, sharks, bony fish and amphibians

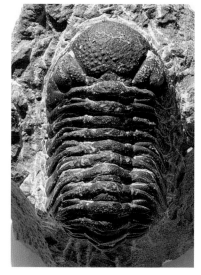

Life in the seas during Devonian times may have been more varied than at any other time in the Palaeozoic Era. On land, plants began to develop and the first amphibians appeared.

Corals remained major reef builders, and trilobites continued to decline in numbers, although some grew to over 70 centimetres in length. During the Devonian Period the brachiopods evolved to become very diverse and abundant. The most numerous of this period were the spiriferids.

Molluscs developed in freshwater as well as in marine sites. Gastropods evolved to be able to cope with a land environment, as did arthropods, producing both millipedes and scorpions. Primitive spiders also evolved. The Devonian Period was the time when fish became abundant in the seas, including species that reached 9 metres long.

This was also the time when the sharks and the bony fish were first found in the seas.

During the Devonian Period, seed plants evolved, so that land plants no longer depended on germination in water.

At the end of this abundant period, there was another mass extinction, with about a quarter of all families dying out. Ammonoids suffered particularly, as did fish and amphibians, and corals and trilobites lost half of their families.

(Above) Devonian trilobite: *Phacops.*

(Below) Silurian trilobite: *Calymene.*

(Below) Devonian spiriferid brachiopod: *Spirifer bollandensis.*

The Carboniferous Period

280 million to 325 million years ago	Molluscs increase, many brachiopods and amphibians die out, coal swamps develop widely. Conifers, insects, amphibians, and reptiles evolve
325 million to 345 million years ago	Crinoids abundant. First seed ferns, ammonoids

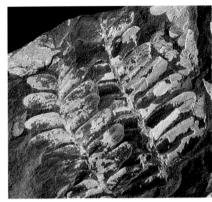

The Lower Carboniferous (also known as the Mississippian in North America) was a time when crinoids became widespread and common enough to be the main limestone-forming fossils.

By the Upper Carboniferous (Pennsylvanian) the crinoids were declining; molluscs increased, as did some brachiopods, especially the productids.

On land, or in coastal swamps, there were large forests, whose buried remains now make up vast beds of coal. The largest trees were lycopods, or scale trees. Another important group on land were the seed ferns, for these developed into flowering plants.

On land, insects diversified and the largest insects ever to have lived, flourished. Dragonflies with a wing span of 75 centimetres were common, and cockroaches reached 10 centimetres in length. Amphibians were, by now, much more common. Also, the first reptiles developed watertight eggs; they no longer had to return to the water to breed, and so they could reach all of the land, while the amphibians had to remain close to water.

(Above) Upper Carboniferous seed fern *Neuropteris.*

The Permian Period

225 million to 280 million years ago	The world's greatest known mass extinction occurs at the end of the Permian with many Palaeozoic Era species becoming extinct, including trilobites; many others reduced greatly in numbers, including ammonoids, brachiopods, crinoids and amphibians

(Below) Permian tree.

In the seas, brachiopods developed long spines, and crinoids were abundant, but the increasingly dry climate over much of the world's land meant that plants declined and many became extinct. One of the more successful were the conifers, since they were more able to adapt to dry conditions.

The dry conditions did not affect the evolution of insects, although they were restricted to being close to sources of water. Reptiles continued to thrive and at this time the sail-backed pelycosaurs developed. Mammals are probably descended from these reptiles. The first mammal-like reptiles were the therapsids. Unlike the reptiles, they were small.

At the end of the Permian Period there was the most severe of all the mass extinctions that had occurred during life on earth. Only four out of every hundred species survived. At this time, the rugose corals became extinct, as did nearly all the brachiopods; molluscs were almost wiped out, as were ammonoids. Trilobites were destroyed completely. Three-quarters of all amphibians and four-fifths of all reptiles became extinct, and many plants also disappeared.

(Above) Jurassic echinoid *Cidaris*.

The Mesozoic Era

The Triassic Period

190 million to 225 million years ago	Mass extinction of tabulate corals, ammonoids, amphibians, reptiles greatly reduced in numbers. Gastropods, bivalves, and ammonoids become more common. First scleractinian corals, dinosaurs, marine reptiles and mammals

The Permian extinction is such a dramatic boundary that it led the early geologists to call the Permian Period the end of the Palaeozoic Era, and the Triassic Period the beginning of a completely new era of life – the Mesozoic Era.

(Below) Jurassic ammonite: *Dactylioceras*.

Although all groups were almost wiped out, some recovered more quickly than others. One of the most successful groups was the ammonoids. They were of little importance in the Palaeozoic Era, but during the Triassic Period they developed into 400 genera. The corals developed into modern forms and recovered, molluscs also began to recover. Brachiopods survived but remained few in number.

On land, conifers and seed plants developed. The Petrified Forest of Arizona has trees of this age,

but it was the reptiles that came to dominate in the Triassic. It was the time when the archosaurs, or ruling reptiles, evolved. The archosaurs include dinosaurs, birds and crocodiles. The first dinosaurs belong to the Late Triassic, as do the ichthyosaurs, marine reptiles that were shaped like dolphins. They were the largest animals in the Triassic world, reaching 9 metres in length. Plesiosaurs that looked like turtles also developed. The mammals that emerged in the Triassic Period were small, about mouse sized.

At the end of the Triassic Period, there was yet another mass extinction, less severe than at the end of the Permian Period, but nevertheless a quarter of all families became extinct.

(Below) Jurassic: vertebra from a dinosaur.

The Jurassic Period

135 million to 190 million years ago	Conifers, ammonoids, belemnoids common in oceans, dinosaurs common on land. **First appearance of crocodiles, flying reptiles, and birds**

During this period the surviving species began to diversify again. Ammonoids again flourished and became important index fossils. Coral reefs developed, and echinoids flourished. Squid-like belemnites also developed widely, reaching as much as 2 metres in length.

Land plants again flourished, and coniferous plants again accumulated in swamps to form important coal deposits.

Reptiles were still the dominant group of land animals despite their setback at the end of the Triassic Period. *Stegosaurus* is a member of an order of dinosaurs that evolved during the Jurassic Period. They are distinctive dinosaurs because of the row of triangular plates down their spines.

In the seas, ichthyosaurs continued to dominate, growing to 15 metres long. By the end of the Jurassic Period, they had been overtaken in importance by the similar-sized plesiosaurs.

During the Jurassic Period the first flying reptiles emerged. These are the pterosaurs, featherless but

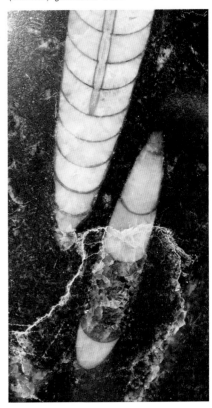

(Below) Jurassic belemnite.

growing to an enormous size, although in the Jurassic Period the largest had a wing span of only 1 metre. *Archaeopteryx*, the first true feathered bird, but still with reptile-like teeth, also evolved during the Jurassic Period.

The Cretaceous Period

65 million to 135 million years ago	Ammonoids, belemnites, flying reptiles, dinosaurs, marine reptiles all become extinct at end of period. Scleractinian corals (hexacorals) develop, gastropods, molluscs, ammonites, belemnites, sponges, dinosaurs are common. First recorded primates, modern fish	

The Cretaceous Period was a long, fairly recent period, when extensive shallow seas produced enormous sheets of rock. Cretaceous rocks are more common than rocks from any other period.

Algae flourished in this time, forming the chalk rocks that are one of the dominant forms of Cretaceous limestone.

All marine life flourished in these seas, and many groups were more abundant at this time than at any other time in their history. Corals, for example, were extremely varied and more important reef builders than today. A group of molluscs, called rudists, were also so prolific that they built huge reefs by cementing their cone-shaped valves together. Ammonoids continued to thrive and are used as index fossils just as they were in the Jurassic Period. Gastropods became more numerous. Echinoids continued to thrive. The modern fishes evolved to dominate the seas.

Of the marine reptiles, the plesiosaurs were replaced by lizard-like mosasaurs which had flippers rather than legs. They reached 17 metres in length. During the Cretaceous Period the pterosaurs became giants, with wing spans of nearly 8 metres. The Cretaceous Period, however, is known for the evolution of *Tyrannosaurus*, the world's largest ever land predator, reaching 14 metres in length and standing over 6 metres high.

(Above) Cretaceous: sponge (*Raphidonema faringdonensis*).

(Above) Cretaceous: ammonite.

(Above) Cretaceous echinoid: *Micraster*.

The end of the Cretaceous Period is marked by another mass extinction. It is the second most devastating extinction after the one at the end of the Permian Period. It marks the end of the Mesozoic Era. About half of all animal families became extinct. The most significant losers included nearly all of the giant reptiles (leaving only the crocodile and turtle), the ammonites and the belemnites. Plants were relatively unscathed, and fishes were not significantly reduced in families. As a result, there was a completely different balance of living things on land at the beginning of the Cenozoic Era.

The Cenozoic Era
The Tertiary Period

Pliocene Epoch 1.6 million to 5 million years ago	Beginning of Ice Age
Miocene Epoch 5 million to 26 million years ago	Largest sharks and whales Early humankind
Oligocene Epoch 26 million to 37.5 million years ago	First recorded occurrence of grasses
Eocene Epoch 37.5 million to 54 million years ago	First recorded large mammals
Paleocene Epoch 54 million to 65 million years ago	Mammals become much more common

With the extinction of large reptiles many remaining families became more abundant. Molluscs and gastropods became numerous, but echinoids and corals were much less common. Mammals developed quickly in this period. Starting as small animals, they became rapidly bigger and more diverse, with legs and arms developed for grasping or running, and specialised teeth. Plant-eaters, such as horses, camels and elephants, were soon followed by hunters such as cats. Hominids – people – developed at the end of the Tertiary Period.

(Below) Tertiary ants in amber.

(Below) Tertiary gastropod.

(Below) Quaternary mammoth tooth.

Glossary

aa lava: a type of lava with a broken, bouldery surface.

abrasion: the rubbing away (erosion) of a rock by the physical scraping of particles carried by water, wind or ice.

acidic rock: a type of igneous rock that consists predominantly of light-coloured minerals and more than two-thirds silica (e.g. granite).

active volcano: a volcano that has observable signs of activity, for example, periodic plumes of steam.

adit: a horizontal tunnel drilled into rock.

aftershock: an earthquake that follows the main shock. Major earthquakes are followed by a number of aftershocks that decrease in frequency with time.

agglomerate: a rock made from the compacted particles thrown out by a volcano (e.g. tuff).

alkaline rock: a type of igneous rock containing less than half silica and normally dominated by dark-coloured minerals (e.g. gabbro).

amygdule: a vesicle in a volcanic rock filled with secondary minerals such as calcite, quartz or zeolite.

andesite: an igneous volcanic rock. Slightly more acidic than basalt.

anticline: an arching fold of rock layers in which the rocks slope down from the crest. See also syncline.

Appalachian Mountain (Orogenic) Belt: an old mountain range that extends for more than 3000 km along the eastern margin of North America from Alabama in the southern United States to Newfoundland, Canada, in the north. There were three Appalachian orogenies: Taconic (about 460 million years ago) in the Ordovician; Acadian (390 to 370 million years ago) in the Devonian; and Alleghenian (300 to 250 million years ago) in the Late Carboniferous to Permian. These mountain belts can be traced as the Caledonian and Hercynian orogenic belts in Europe.

Archean Eon: see eon.

arenaceous: a rock composed largely of sand grains.

argillaceous: a rock composed largely of clay.

arkose: a coarse sandstone formed by the disintegration of a granite.

ash, volcanic: fine powdery material thrown out of a volcano.

asthenosphere: the weak part of the upper mantle below the lithosphere, in which slow convection is thought to take place.

augite: a dark green-coloured silicate mineral containing calcium, sodium, iron, aluminium and magnesium.

axis of symmetry: a line or plane around which one part of a crystal is a mirror image of another part.

basalt: basic fine-grained igneous volcanic rock; lava often contains vesicles.

basic rock: an igneous rock (e.g. gabbro) with silica content less than two-thirds and containing a high percentage of dark-coloured minerals.

basin: a large, circular, or oval sunken region on the earth's surface created by downwards folding. A river basin, or watershed, is the area drained by a river and its tributaries.

batholith: a very large body of plutonic rock that was intruded deep into the earth's crust and is now exposed by erosion.

bauxite: a surface material that contains a high percentage of aluminium silicate. The principal ore of aluminium.

bed: a layer of sediment. It may involve many phases of deposition, each marked by a bedding plane.

bedding plane: an ancient surface on which sediment built up. Sedimentary rocks often split along bedding planes.

biotite: a black-coloured form of mica.

body wave: a seismic wave that can travel through the interior of the earth. P waves and S waves are body waves.

boss: an upwards extension of a batholith. A boss may once have been a magma chamber.

botryoidal: the shape of a mineral that resembles a bunch of grapes, e.g. haematite the crystals of which are often arranged in massive clumps, giving a surface covered with spherical bulges.

butte: a small mesa.

calcareous: composed mainly of calcium carbonate.

calcite: a mineral composed of calcium carbonate.

caldera: the collapsed cone of a volcano. It sometimes contains a crater lake.

Caledonian Mountain-Building Period, Caledonian Orogeny: a major mountain-building period in the Lower Paleozoic Era that reached its climax at the end of the Silurian Period (430 to 395 million years ago). An early phase affected only North America and made part of the Appalachian Mountain Belt.

Cambrian, Cambrian Period: the first period of geological time in the Paleozoic Era, beginning 570 million years ago and ending 500 million years ago.

carbonate minerals: minerals formed with carbonate ions (e.g. calcite).

Carboniferous, Carboniferous Period: a period of geological time between about 345 and 280 million years ago. It is often divided into the Early Carboniferous Epoch (345 to 320 million years ago) and the Late Carboniferous Epoch (320 to 280 million years ago). The Late Carboniferous is characterised by large coal-forming swamps. In North America the Carboniferous is usually divided into the Mississippian (= Lower Carboniferous) and Pennsylvanian (= Upper Carboniferous) periods.

cast, fossil: the natural filling of a mould by sediment or minerals that were left when a fossil dissolved after being enclosed by rock.

Cenozoic, Cenozoic Era: the most recent era of geological time, beginning 65 million years ago and continuing to the present.

central vent volcano: see stratovolcano.

chemical compound: a substance made from the chemical combination of two or more elements.

chemical rock: a rock produced by chemical precipitation (e.g. halite).

chemical weathering: the decay of a rock through the chemical action of water containing dissolved acidic gases.

cinder cone: a volcanic cone made entirely of cinders. Cinder cones have very steep sides.

class: the level of biological classification below a phylum.

clast: an individual grain of a rock.

clastic rock: a sedimentary rock that is made up of fragments of pre-existing rocks, carried by gravity, water, or wind (e.g. conglomerate, sandstone).

cleavage: the tendency of some minerals to break along one or more smooth surfaces.

coal: the carbon-rich, solid mineral derived from fossilised plant remains. Found in sedimentary rocks. Types of coal include bituminous, brown, lignite, and anthracite. A fossil fuel.

complex volcano: a volcano that has had an eruptive history and which produces two or more vents.

composite volcano: see stratovolcano.

concordant coast: a coast where the geological structure is parallel to the coastline. See also discordant coastline.

conduction (of heat): the transfer of heat between touching objects.

conglomerate: a coarse-grained sedimentary rock with grains larger than 2 mm.

contact metamorphism: metamorphism that occurs owing to direct contact with a molten magma. See also regional metamorphism.

continental drift: the theory suggested by Alfred Wegener that earth's continents were originally one land mass which split up to form the arrangement of continents we see today.

continental shelf: the ocean floor from the coastal shore of continents to the continental slope.

continental shield: the ancient and stable core of a tectonic plate. Also called a shield.

convection: the slow overturning of a liquid or gas that is heated from below.

cordillera: a long mountain belt consisting of many mountain ranges.

core: the innermost part of the earth. The earth's core is very dense, rich in iron, partly molten, and the source of the earth's magnetic field. The inner core is solid and has a radius of about 1300 kilometres. The outer core is fluid and is about 2100 kilometres thick. S waves cannot travel through the outer core.

cracking: the breaking up of a hydrocarbon compound into simpler constituents by means of heat.

crater lake: a lake found inside a caldera.

craton: *see* shield.

Cretaceous, Cretaceous Period: the third period of the Mesozoic Era. It lasted from about 135 to 65 million years ago. It was a time of chalk formation and when many dinosaurs lived.

cross-bedding: a pattern of deposits in a sedimentary rock in which many thin layers lie at an angle to the bedding planes, showing that the sediment was deposited by a moving fluid. Wind-deposited cross-beds are often bigger than water-deposited beds.

crust: the outermost layer of the earth, typically 5 km under the oceans and 50 to 100 km thick under continents. It makes up less than 1 per cent of the earth's volume.

crustal plate: *see* tectonic plate.

crystal: a mineral that has a regular geometric shape and is bounded by smooth, flat faces.

crystal system: a group of crystals with the same arrangement of axes.

crystalline: a mineral that has solidified but has been unable to produce well-formed crystals. Quartz and halite are commonly found as crystalline masses.

crystallisation: the formation of crystals.

cubic: a crystal system in which crystals have 3 axes all at right angles to one another and of equal length.

cuesta: a ridge in the landscape formed by a resistant band of dipping rock. A cuesta has a steep scarp slope and a more gentle dip slope.

current bedding: a pattern of deposits in a sedimentary rock in which many thin layers lie at an angle to the bedding planes, showing that the sediment was deposited by a current of water.

cyclothem: a repeating sequence of rocks found in coal strata.

delta: a triangle of deposition produced where a river enters a sea or lake.

deposit, deposition: the process of laying down material that has been transported in suspension or solution by water, ice, or wind. A deposit is the material laid down by deposition (e.g. salt deposits).

destructive plate boundary: a line where plates collide and where one plate is subducted into the mantle.

Devonian, Devonian Period: the fourth period of geological time in the Palaeozoic Era, from 395 to 345 million years ago.

diorite: an igneous plutonic rock between gabbro and granite; the plutonic equivalent of andesite.

dip: the angle that a bedding plane or fault makes with the horizontal.

dip slope: the more gently sloping part of a cuesta whose surface often parallels the dip of the strata.

discontinuity: a gap in deposition, perhaps caused by the area being lifted above the sea so that erosion, rather than deposition, occurred for a time.

discordant coast: a coast where the rock structure is at an angle to the line of the coast. *See also* concordant coastline.

displacement: the distance over which one piece of rock is pushed relative to another.

dissolve: to break down a substance into a solution without causing a reaction.

distillation: the boiling off of volatile materials, leaving a residue.

dolomite: a mineral composed of calcium magnesium carbonate.

dome: a circular, uplifted region of rocks taking the shape of a dome and found in some areas of folded rocks. Rising plugs of salt will also dome up the rocks above them. They sometimes make oil traps.

dormant volcano: a volcano that shows no signs of activity but which has been active in the recent past.

drift: a tunnel drilled in rock and designed to provide a sloping route for carrying out ore or coal by means of a conveyor belt.

dyke: a wall-like sheet of igneous rock that cuts across the layers of the surrounding rocks.

dyke swarm: a collection of hundreds or thousands of parallel dykes.

earthquake: shaking of the earth's surface caused by a sudden movement of rock within the earth.

element: a fundamental chemical building block. A substance that cannot be separated into simpler substances by any chemical means. Oxygen and sulphur are examples of elements.

eon: the largest division of geological time. An eon is subdivided into eras. Precambrian time is divided into the Archean (earlier than 2.5 billion years ago) and Proterozoic eons (more recent than 2.5 billion years ago). The Phanerozoic Eon includes the Cambrian Period to the present.

epicentre: the point on the earth's surface directly above the focus (hypocentre) of an earthquake.

epoch: a subdivision of a geological period in the geological time scale (e.g. Pleistocene Epoch).

era: a subdivision of a geological eon in the geological time scale (e.g. Cenozoic Era). An era is subdivided into periods.

erode, erosion: the twin processes of breaking down a rock (called weathering) and then removing the debris (called transporting).

escarpment: the crest of a ridge made of dipping rocks.

essential mineral: the dominant mineral constituents of a rock used to classify it.

evaporite: a mineral or rock formed as the result of evaporation of salt-laden water, such as a lagoon or salt lake.

exoskeleton: another word for shell. Applies to invertebrates.

extinct volcano: a volcano that has shown no signs of activity in historic times.

extrusive rock, extrusion: an igneous volcanic rock that has solidified on the surface of the earth.

facet: the cleaved face of a mineral. Used in describing jewellery.

facies: physical, chemical, or biological variations in a sedimentary bed of the same geological age (e.g. sandy facies, limestone facies).

family: a part of the classification of living things above a genus.

fault: a deep fracture or zone of fractures in rocks along which there has been displacement of one side relative to the other. It represents a weak point in the crust and upper mantle.

fault scarp: a long, straight, steep slope in the landscape that has been produced by faulting.

feldspar: the most common silicate mineral. It consists of two forms: plagioclase and orthoclase.

ferromagnesian mineral: dark-coloured minerals, such as augite and hornblende, which contain relatively high proportions of iron and magnesium and low proportions of silica.

fissure: a substantial crack in a rock.

fjord: a glaciated valley in a mountainous area coastal area that has been partly flooded by the sea.

focal depth: the depth of an earthquake focus below the surface.

focus: the origin of an earthquake, directly below the epicentre.

fold: arched or curved rock strata.

fold axis: line following the highest arching in an anticline, or the lowest arching in a syncline.

fold belt: a part of a mountain system containing folded sedimentary rocks.

foliation: a texture of a rock (usually schist) that resembles the pages in a book.

formation: a word used to describe a collection of related rock layers or beds. A number of related beds make a member; a collection of related members makes up a formation. Formations are often given location names, e.g. Toroweap Formation, the members of which are a collection of dominantly limestone beds.

fossil: any evidence of past life, including remains, traces and imprints.

fossil fuel: any fuel that was formed in the geological past from the remains of living organisms. The main fossil fuels are coal and petroleum (oil and natural gas).

fraction: one of the components of crude oil that can be separated from others by heating and then by cooling the vapour.

fracture: a substantial break across a rock.

fracture zone: a region in which fractures are common. Fracture zones are particularly common in folded rock and near faults.

frost shattering: the process of breaking pieces of rock through the action of freezing and melting of rainwater

gabbro: alkaline igneous plutonic rock, typically showing dark-coloured crystals; plutonic equivalent of basalt.

gallery: a horizontal access tunnel in a mine.

gangue: the unwanted mineral matter found in association with a metal.

gem: a mineral, usually in crystal form, that is regarded as having particular beauty and value.

genus: (*pl.* genera) the biological classification for a group of closely related species.

geode: a hollow lump of rock (nodule) that often contains crystals.

geological column: a columnar diagram showing the divisions of geological time (eons, eras, periods, and epochs).

geological eon: *see* eon.

geological epoch: *see* epoch.

geological era: *see* era.

geological period: a subdivision of a geological era (e.g. Carboniferous Period). A period is subdivided into epochs.

geological system: a term for an accumulation of strata that occurs during a geological period (e.g. the Ordovician System is the rocks deposited during the Ordovician Period). Systems are divided into series.

geological time: the history of the earth revealed by its rocks.

geological time scale: the division of geological time into eons, era, periods, and epochs.

geosyncline: a large, slowly subsiding region marginal to a continent where huge amounts of sediment accumulate. The rocks in a geosyncline are eventually lifted to form mountain belts.

gneiss: a metamorphic rock showing large grains.

graben: a fallen block of the earth's crust forming a long trough, separated on all sides by faults. Associated with rift valleys.

grain: a particle of a rock or mineral.

granite: an acidic, igneous, plutonic rock containing free quartz, typically light in colour; plutonic equivalent of rhyolite.

grit: grains larger than sand but smaller than stones.

groundmass: *see* matrix.

group: a word used to describe a collection of related rock layers, or beds. A number of related beds make a member; a collection of related members makes up a formation; a collection of related formations makes a group.

gypsum: a mineral made of calcium sulphate.

halide minerals: a group of minerals (e.g. halite) that contain a halogen element (elements similar to chlorine) bonded with another element. Many are evaporite minerals.

halite: a mineral made of sodium chloride.

Hawaiian-type eruption: a name for a volcanic eruption that mainly consists of lava fountains.

hexagonal: a crystal system in which crystals have 3 axes all at 120 degrees to one another and of equal length.

hogback: a cuesta where the scarp and dip slopes are at about the same angle.

hornblende: a dark-green silicate mineral of the amphibole group containing sodium, potassium, calcium, magnesium, iron and aluminium.

horst: a raised block of the earth's crust separated on all sides by faults. Associated with rift valleys.

hot spot: a place where a fixed mantle magma plume reaches the surface.

hydraulic action: the erosive action of water pressure on rocks.

hydrothermal: a change brought about in a rock or mineral due to the action of superheated mineral-rich fluids, usually water.

hypocentre: the calculated location of the focus of an earthquake.

ice wedging: *see* frost shattering.

Icelandic-type eruption: a name given to a fissure type of eruption.

igneous rock: rock formed by the solidification of magma. Igneous rocks include volcanic and plutonic rocks.

impermeable: a rock that will not allow a liquid to pass through it.

imprint: a cast left by a former life form.

impurities: small amounts of elements or compounds in an otherwise homogeneous mineral.

index fossil: a fossil used as a marker for a particular part of geological time.

intrusive rock, intrusion: rocks that have formed from cooling magma below the surface. When inserted amongst other rocks, intruded rocks are called an intrusion.

invertebrate: an animal with an external skeleton.

ion: a charged particle.

island arc: a pattern of volcanic islands that follows the shape of an arc when seen from above.

isostacy: the principle that a body can float in a more dense fluid. The same as buoyancy, but used for continents.

joint: a significant crack between blocks of rock, normally used in the context of patterns of cracks.

Jurassic, Jurassic Period: the second geological period in the Mesozoic Era, lasting from about 190 to 135 million years ago.

kingdom: the broadest division in the biological classification of living things.

laccolith: a lens-shaped body of intrusive igneous rock with a dome-shaped upper surface and a flat bottom surface.

landform: a recognisable shape of part of the landscape, for example, a cuesta.

landslide: the rapid movement of a slab of soil down a steep hillslope.

lateral fault: *see* thrust fault.

laterite: a surface deposit containing a high proportion of iron.

lava: molten rock material extruded onto the surface of the earth.

lava bomb: *see* volcanic bomb.

law of superposition: the principle that younger rock is deposited on older.

limestone: a carbonate sedimentary rock composed of more than half calcium carbonate.

lithosphere: that part of the crust and upper mantle which is brittle and makes up the tectonic plates.

lode: a mining term for a rock containing many rich ore-bearing minerals. Similar to vein.

Love wave, L wave: a major type of surface earthquake wave that shakes the ground surface at right angles to the direction in which the wave is travelling. It is named after A.E.H. Love, the English mathematician who discovered it.

lustre: the way in which a mineral reflects light. Used as a test when identifying minerals.

magma: the molten material that comes from the mantle and which cools to form igneous rocks.

magma chamber: a large cavity melted in the earth's crust and filled with magma. Many magma chambers are plumes of magma that have melted their way from the mantle to the upper part of the crust. When a magma chamber is no longer supplied with molten magma, the magma solidifies to form a granite batholith.

mantle: the layer of the earth between the crust and the core. It is approximately 2900 kilometres thick and is the largest of the earth's major layers.

marginal accretion: the growth of mountain belts on the edges of a shield.

mass extinction: a time when the majority of species on the planet were killed off.

matrix: the rock or sediment in which a fossil is embedded; the fine-grained rock in which larger particles are embedded, for example, in a conglomerate.

mechanical weathering: the disintegration of a rock by frost shattering/ice wedging.

mesa: a large detached piece of a tableland.

Mesozoic, Mesozoic Era: the geological era between the Palaeozoic and the Cenozoic eras. It lasted from about 225 to 65 million years ago.

metamorphic aureole: the region of contact metamorphic rock that surrounds a batholith.

metamorphic rock: any rock (e.g. schist, gneiss) that was formed from a pre-existing rock by heat and pressure.

meteorite: a substantial chunk of rock in space.

micas: a group of soft, sheet-like silicate minerals (e.g. biotite, muscovite).

mid-ocean ridge: a long mountain chain on the ocean floor where basalt periodically erupts, forming new oceanic crust.

mineral: a naturally occurring inorganic substance of definite chemical composition (e.g. calcite, calcium carbonate).
    More generally, any resource extracted from the ground by mining (includes metal ores, coal, oil, gas, rocks, etc.).

mineral environment: the place where a mineral or a group of associated minerals form. Mineral environments include igneous, sedimentary, and metamorphic rocks.

mineralisation: the formation of minerals within a rock.

Modified Mercalli Scale: a scale for measuring the impact of an earthquake. It is composed of 12 increasing levels of intensity, which range from imperceptible, designated by Roman numeral I, to catastrophic destruction, designated by XII.

Mohorovicic discontinuity: the boundary surface that separates the earth's crust from the underlying mantle. Named after Andrija Mohorovicic, a Croatian seismologist.

Mohs' Scale of Hardness: a relative scale developed to put minerals into an order. The hardest is 10 (diamond), and the softest is 1 (talc).

monoclinic: a crystal system in which crystals have 2 axes all at right angles to one another, and each axis is of unequal length.

mould: an impression in a rock of the outside of an organism.

mountain belt: a region where there are many ranges of mountains. The term is often applied to a wide belt of mountains produced during mountain building.

mountain building: the creation of mountains as a result of the collision of tectonic plates. Long belts or chains of mountains can form along the edge of a continent during this process. Mountain building is also called orogeny.

mountain building period: a period during which a geosyncline is compressed into fold mountains by the collision of two tectonic plates. Also known as orogenesis.

mudstone: a fine-grained, massive rock formed by the compaction of mud.

nappe: a piece of a fold that has become detached from its roots during intensive mountain building.

native metal: a metal that occurs uncombined with any other element.

natural gas: *see* petroleum.

normal fault: a fault in which one block has slipped down the face of another. It is the most common kind of fault and results from tension.

nueé ardente: another word for pyroclastic flow.

ocean trench: a deep, steep-sided trough in the ocean floor caused by the subduction of oceanic crust beneath either other oceanic crust or continental crust.

olivine: the name of a group of magnesium iron silicate minerals that have an olive colour.

order: a level of biological classification between class and family.

Ordovician, Ordovician Period: the second period of geological time within the Palaeozoic Era. It lasted from about 500 to 430 million years ago.

ore: a rock containing enough useful metal or fuel to be worth mining.

ore mineral: a mineral that occurs in sufficient quantity to be mined for its metal. The compound must also be easy to process.

organic rocks: rocks formed by living things, for example, coal.

orthoclase: the form of feldspar that is often pink in colour and which contains potassium as important ions.

orogenic belt: a mountain belt.

orogeny: a period of mountain building. Orogenesis is the process of mountain building and the creation of orogenic belts.

orthorhombic: a crystal system in which crystals have 3 axes all at right angles to one another but of unequal length.

outcrop: the exposure of a rock at the surface of the earth.

overburden: the unwanted layer(s) of rock above an ore or coal body.

oxide minerals: a group of minerals in which oxygen is a major constituent. A compound in which oxygen is bonded to another element or group.

Pacific Ring of Fire: the ring of volcanoes and volcanic activity that circles the Pacific Ocean. Created by the collision of the Pacific Plate with its neighbouring plates.

pahoehoe lava: the name for a form of lava that has a smooth surface.

Palaeozoic, Palaeozoic Era: a major interval of geological time. The Palaeozoic is the oldest era in which fossil life is commonly found. It lasted from about 570 to 225 million years ago.

palaeomagnetism: the natural magnetic traces that reveal the intensity and direction of the earth's magnetic field in the geological past.

pegmatite: an igneous rock (e.g. a dyke) of extremely coarse crystals.

Pelean-type eruption: a violent explosion dominated by pyroclastic flows.

period: *see* geological period.

permeable rock: a rock that will allow a fluid to pass through it.

Permian, Permian Period: the last period of the Palaeozoic Era, lasting from about 280 to 225 million years ago.

petrified: when the tissues of a dead plant or animal have been replaced by minerals, such as silica, they are said to be petrified (e.g. petrified wood).

petrified forest: a large number of fossil trees. Most petrified trees are replaced by silica.

petroleum: the carbon-rich, and mostly liquid, mixture produced by the burial and partial alteration of animal and plant remains. Petroleum is found in many sedimentary rocks. The liquid part of petroleum is called oil, the gaseous part is known as natural gas. Petroleum is an important fossil fuel.

petroleum field: a region from which petroleum can be recovered.

Phanerozoic Eon: the most recent eon, beginning at the Cambrian Period, some 570 million years ago, and extending up to the present.

phenocryst: an especially large crystal (in a porphyritic rock), embedded in smaller mineral grains.

phylum: (*pl.* phyla) biological classification for one of the major divisions of animal life and second in complexity to kingdom. The plant kingdom is not divided into phyla but into divisions.

placer deposit: a sediment containing heavy metal grains (e.g. gold) that have weathered out of the bedrock and are concentrated on a stream bed or along a coast.

plagioclase: the form of feldspar that is often white or grey and which contains sodium and calcium as important ions.

planetismals: small embryo planets.

plate: *see* tectonic plate.

plateau: an extensive area of raised flat land. The cliff-like edges of a plateau may, when eroded, leave isolated features such as mesas and buttes. *See also* tableland.

plate tectonics: the theory that the earth's crust and upper mantle (the lithosphere) are broken into a number of more or less rigid, but constantly moving, slabs or plates.

Plinian-type eruption: an explosive eruption that sends a column of ash high into the air.

plug: *see* volcanic plug

plunging fold: a fold whose axis dips, or plunges, into the ground.

plutonic rock: an igneous rock that has solidified at great depth and contains large crystals due to the slowness of cooling (e.g. granite, gabbro).

porphyry, porphyritic rock: an igneous rock in which larger crystals (phenocrysts) are enclosed in a fine-grained matrix.

Precambrian, Precambrian time: the whole of earth history before the Cambrian Period. Also called Precambrian Era and Precambrian Eon.

precipitate: a substance that has settled out of a liquid as a result of a chemical reaction between two chemicals in the liquid.

Primary Era: an older name for the Palaeozoic Era.

prismatic: a word used to describe a mineral that has formed with one axis very much longer than the others.

Proterozoic Eon: *see* eon.

P wave, primary wave, primary seismic wave: P waves are the fastest body waves. The waves carry energy in the same line as the direction of the wave. P waves can travel through all layers of the earth and are generally felt as a thump. *See also* S wave.

pyrite: iron sulphide. It is common in sedimentary rocks that were poor in oxygen, and sometimes forms fossil casts.

pyroclastic flow: solid material ejected from a volcano, combined with searingly hot gases, which together behave as a high-density fluid. Pyroclastic flows can do immense damage, as was the case with Mount Saint Helens.

pyroclastic material: any solid material ejected from a volcano.

Quaternary, Quaternary Period: the second period in the Cenozoic Era, beginning about 1.6 million years ago and continuing to the present day.

radiation: the transfer of energy between objects that are not in contact.

radioactive dating: the dating of a material by the use of its radioactive elements. The rate of decay of any element changes in a predictable way, allowing a precise date to be given of when the material was formed.

rank: a name used to describe the grade of coal in terms of its possible heat output. The higher the rank, the more the heat output.

Rayleigh wave: a type of surface wave having an elliptical motion similar to the waves caused when a stone is dropped into a pond. It is the slowest, but often the largest and most destructive, of the wave types caused by an earthquake. It is usually felt as a rolling or rocking motion and, in the case of major earthquakes, can be seen as they approach. Named after Lord Rayleigh, the English physicist who predicted its existence.

regional metamorphism: metamorphism resulting from both heat and pressure. It is usually connected with mountain building and occurs over a large area. *See also* contact metamorphism.

reniform: a kidney-shaped mineral habit (e.g. hematite).

reservoir rock: a permeable rock in which petroleum accumulates.

reversed fault: a fault where one slab of the earth's crust rides up over another. Reversed faults are only common during plate collision.

rhyolite: acid, igneous, volcanic rock, typically light in colour; volcanic equivalent of granite.

ria: the name for a partly flooded coastal river valley in an area where the landscape is hilly.

Richter Scale: the system used to measure the strength of an earthquake. Developed by Charles Richter, an American, in 1935.

rift, rift valley: long troughs on continents and mid-ocean ridges that are bounded by normal faults.

rifting: the process of crustal stretching that causes blocks of crust to subside, creating rift valleys.

rock: a naturally occurring solid material containing one or more minerals.

rock cycle: the continuous sequence of events that cause mountains to be formed, then eroded, before being formed again.

rupture: the place over which an earthquake causes rocks to move against one another.

salt dome: a balloon-shaped mass of salt produced by salt being forced upwards under pressure.

sandstone: a sedimentary rock composed of cemented sand-sized grains 0.06–2 mm in diameter.

scarp slope: the steep slope of a cuesta.

schist: a metamorphic rock characterised by a shiny surface of mica crystals all orientated in the same direction.

scoria: the rough, often foam-like rock that forms on the surface of some lavas.

seamount: a volcano that rises from the sea bed.

Secondary Era: an older term for a geological era. Now replaced by Mesozoic Era.

sediment: any solid material that has settled out of suspension in a liquid.

sedimentary rock: a layered clastic rock formed through the deposition of pieces of mineral, rock, animal or vegetable matter.

segregation: the separation of minerals.

seismic gap: a part of an active fault where there have been no earthquakes in recent times.

seismic wave: a wave generated by an earthquake.

series: the rock layers that correspond to an epoch of time.

shadow zone: the region of the earth that experiences no shocks after an earthquake.

shaft: a vertical tunnel that provides access or ventilation to a mine.

shale: a fine-grained sedimentary rock made of clay minerals with particle sizes smaller than 2 microns.

shield: the ancient and stable core of a tectonic plate. Also called a continental shield.

shield volcano: a volcano with a broad, low-angled cone made entirely of lava.

silica, silicate: silica is silicon dioxide. It is a very common mineral, occurring as quartz, chalcedony, etc. A silicate is any mineral that contains silica.

sill: a tabular, sheet-like body of intrusive igneous rock that has been injected between layers of sedimentary or metamorphic rock.

Silurian, Silurian Period: the name of the third geological period of the Palaeozoic Era. It began about 430 and ended about 395 million years ago.

skarn: a mineral deposit formed by the chemical reaction of hot acidic fluids and carbonate rocks.

slag: waste rock material that becomes separated from the metal during smelting.

slate: a low-grade metamorphic rock produced by pressure, in which the clay minerals have arranged themselves parallel to one another.

slaty cleavage: a characteristic pattern found in slates in which the parallel arrangement of clay minerals causes the rock to fracture (cleave) in sheets.

species: a population of animals or plants capable of interbreeding.

spreading boundary: a line where two plates are being pulled away from each other. New crust is formed as molten rock is forced upwards into the gap.

stock: a vertical protrusion of a batholith that pushes up closer to the surface.

stratigraphy: the study of the earth's rocks in the context of their history and conditions of formation.

stratovolcano: a tall volcanic mountain made of alternating layers, or strata, of ash and lava.

stratum: (*pl.* strata) a layer of sedimentary rock.

streak: the colour of the powder of a mineral produced by rubbing the mineral against a piece of unglazed, white porcelain. Used as a test when identifying minerals.

striation: minute parallel grooves on crystal faces.

strike, direction of: the direction of a bedding plane or fault at right angles to the dip.

Strombolian-type eruption: a kind of volcanic eruption that is explosive enough to send out some volcanic bombs.

subduction: the process of one tectonic plate descending beneath another.

subduction zone: the part of the earth's surface along which one tectonic plate descends into the mantle. It is often shaped in the form of an number of arcs.

sulphides: a group of important ore minerals (e.g. pyrite, galena, and sphalerite) in which sulphur combines with one or more metals.

surface wave: any one of a number of waves such as Love waves or Rayleigh waves that shake the ground surface just after an earthquake. *See also* Love waves and Rayleigh waves.

suture: the junction of 2 or more parts of a skeleton; in cephalopods the junction of a septum with the inner surface of the shell wall. It is very distinctive in ammonoids and used to identify them.

S wave, shear or secondary seismic wave: this kind of wave carries energy through the earth like a rope being shaken. S waves cannot travel through the outer core of the earth because they cannot pass through fluids. *See also* P wave.

syncline: a downfold of rock layers in which the rocks slope up from the bottom of the fold. *See also* anticline.

system: *see* geological system.

tableland: another word for a plateau. *See* plateau.

tectonic plate: one of the great slabs, or plates, of the lithosphere (the earth's crust and part of the earth's upper mantle) that covers the whole of the earth's surface. The earth's plates are separated by zones of volcanic and earthquake activity.

Tertiary, Tertiary Period: the first period of the Cenozoic Era. It began 665 and ended about 1.6 million years ago.

thrust fault: *see* reversed fault.

transcurrent fault: *see* lateral fault.

transform fault: *see* lateral fault.

translucent: a description of a mineral that allows light to penetrate but not pass through.

transparent: a description of a mineral that allows light to pass right through.

trellis drainage pattern: a river drainage system where the trunk river and its tributaries tend to meet at right angles.

trench: *see* ocean trench.

Triassic, Triassic Period: the first period of the Mesozoic era. It lasted from about 225 to 190 million years ago.

triclinic: a crystal system in which crystals have 3 axes, none at right angles or of equal length to one another.

tsunami: a very large wave produced by an underwater earthquake.

tuff: a rock made from volcanic ash.

unconformity: any interruption in the depositional sequence of sedimentary rocks.

valve: in bivalves and brachiopods, one of the separate parts of the shell.

vein: a sheet-like body of mineral matter (e.g. quartz) that cuts across a rock. Veins are often important sources of valuable minerals. Miners call such important veins lodes.

vent: the vertical pipe that allows the passage of magma through the centre of a volcano.

vertebrate: an animal with an internal skeleton.

vesicle: a small cavity in a volcanic rock originally created by an air bubble trapped in the molten lava.

viscous, viscosity: sticky, stickiness.

volatile: substances that tend to evaporate or boil off of a liquid.

volcanic: anything from, or of, a volcano. Volcanic rocks are igneous rocks that cool as they are released at the earth's surface – including those formed underwater; typically have small crystals due to the rapid cooling, e.g. basalt, andesite and rhyolite.

volcanic bomb: a large piece of magma thrown out of a crater during an eruption, which solidifies as it travels through cool air.

volcanic eruption: an ejection of ash or lava from a volcano.

volcanic glass: lava that has solidified very quickly and has not had time to develop any crystals. Obsidian is a volcanic glass.

volcanic plug: the solidified core of an extinct volcano.

Vulcanian-type eruption: an explosive form of eruption without a tall ash column or pyroclastic flow.

water gap: a gap cut by a superimposed river, which is still occupied by the river.

weather, weathered, weathering: the process of weathering is the mechanical action of ice and the chemical action of rainwater on rock, breaking it down into small pieces that can then be carried away. *See also* chemical weathering and mechanical weathering.

wind gap: a gap cut by a superimposed river, which is no longer occupied by the river.

Set Index

USING THE SET INDEX

This index covers all eight volumes in the *Earth Science* set:

Volume number	Title
1:	Minerals
2:	Rocks
3:	Fossils
4:	Earthquakes and volcanoes
5:	Plate tectonics
6:	Landforms
7:	Geological time
8:	The earth's resources

An example entry:

Index entries are listed alphabetically.

plagioclase feldspar **1:** *51*; **2:** 10 *see also* feldspars

Volume numbers are in bold and are followed by page references. Articles on a subject are shown by italic page numbers.

In the example above, 'plagioclase feldspar' appears in Volume 1: Minerals on page 51 as a full article and in Volume 2: Rocks on page 10. Many terms also are covered in the GLOSSARY on pages 60–65.

The *see also* refers to another entry where there will be additional relevant information.

A

aa lava **2:** 24; **4:** 37, 44
abrasion **6:** 41
Aconcagua, Mount (Argentina) **5:** 38
Adirondacks, Adirondack Mountains (New York) **7:** 27
adit **8:** 39, 46
African Plate **5:** 11, 50
African Shield **5:** 54, 55, 56
aftershocks **4:** 14, 15
agate **1:** *50*
Agathla Peak (Arizona) **6:** 55
agglomerate **2:** 18
Agricola **1:** 30
Alaska **5:** 35
    1964 earthquake **4:** 9, 10, 12, *22–25*
    oil fields **8:** 37
Alethopteris **3:** 49
Aleutian Islands (Alaska) **5:** 34, 35
algae **3:** 48, 51
Alleghenian Mountain Building Period **7:** 41
almandine garnet **1:** 52
Alps **5:** 44, 45–51; **7:** 54, 56

B

aluminium **1:** 7; **8:** 8, 11, 33
    ores **8:** *12*
amber, fossils in **3:** 10, 38, 59
amethyst **1:** 5, *48*, 49
ammonites **3:** 4, 15, 16, 24, *26–28*, 56, 58, 59
    recognising fossils **3:** 27
ammonoids **3:** *26–28*, 54, 55, 56, 57, 58
Ampato (Peru) **5:** 37
amphibians **3:** 42, 46, 54, 55, 56
amphiboles **1:** *56*; **2:** 12
amygdules **2:** 16
Anchorage (Alaska) **4:** 22, 23, 25
andalusite **1:** *52*
Andes Mountains, Andes (South America) **5:** 11, *36–38*
andesite **2:** 16, 18, 21, *23*; **4:** 38, 39
Angara Shield **5:** 57
anhydrite **1:** *46*
Annularia **3:** 49
Antarctic Plate **5:** 11
Antarctica **5:** 45
anthracite **8:** 28, 29
anticlines **6:** 37, 38, 39; **8:** 32
antimony **8:** 10
apatite **1:** 23, *47*
apophylite **1:** 24
Appalachian Mountain Belt **5:** 45
Appalachian Mountains, Appalachians (United States) **5:** 44, 45; **6:** 36, 37, 38, 39, 40; **7:** 29, 30, 41, 53
    coal fields **8:** 35
aquamarine **1:** 25, *55*
Arabian Plate **5:** 11
aragonite **1:** 28, *44*
Archaeopteryx **3:** 58
Archean Eon **7:** 25
Arches National Park (Utah) **6:** 20
arches, coastal **6:** 41–46
archosaurs **3:** 57
Arduino, Giovanni **7:** 15
arenaceous rocks **2:** 42
argillaceous sandstone **2:** 43
arkose sandstone **2:** 42, 44
arsenic **1:** 31; **8:** 10, 45, 57
arthropods (Arthropoda) **3:** *38–41*, 51, 53, 54
Articulatean **3:** 48
Arun River (Nepal) **6:** 10
ash, volcanic **2:** 16, 18, 19; **4:** 35, 36; **6:** 24, 55
asthenosphere **5:** 6, 8, 9
Atlantic Ocean **5:** 23, 25; **7:** 50, 55, 57
    oil fields **8:** 37
Atlantis, research ship **5:** 25
Atlas Mountains (Morocco) **7:** 54
atmosphere, formation **7:** 24–27
augen gneiss **2:** 59
augite **1:** 7, 14, 16, *56*; **2:** 12
Australian Shield **5:** 54, 56, 57
Ayers Rock (Australia) **5:** 57
azurite **1:** 20, *44*

B

Baltic Shield **5:** 57; **7:** 25
Baltica **7:** 30, 32, 34, 36, 39
banded gneiss **2:** 59
barite **1:** 27, *46*
basalt **1:** 12; **2:** 14, 15, 17, 20, 21, *23–25*; **4:** 37, 38, 39, 42, 44, 46, 47, 48, 49; **5:** 25; **6:** 53, 54; **8:** 8

basalt columns **2:** 15, 25; **6:** 18, 26
Basin and Range **4:** 27, 28; **5:** 42; **6:** 49
basins **6:** 40
batholiths **1:** 11; **6:** 19, 52, 53, 59
    ore minerals **8:** 24
Bauer, Georg **1:** 30
bauxite **1:** *39*; **8:** *12*, 33, 41
bedding, bedding planes **2:** 32, 36, 37; **6:** 20, 32
belemnites (Belemnoids) **3:** 4, *24–25*, 57, 58, 59
    recognising fossils **3:** 24
Bendigo (Australia) **7:** 35; **8:** 43
Bennetitalean **3:** 48
beryl **1:** 27, *55*
Berzelius, Jons **1:** 30
Big Bend National Park (Texas) **5:** 13; **6:** 58
biotite **1:** *58*; **2:** 11 *see also* mica
birds **3:** 42, 57, 58
bismuth **1:** 31; **8:** 10
bituminous coal **8:** 28, 29, 36*(map)*
bivalves (Bivalvia) **3:** *29–31*, 52, 56
    recognising fossils **3:** 30
bloodstone **1:** 50
Blue Ridge Mountains (United States) **5:** 45
body waves **4:** 8 *see also* P and S waves
bony fish **3:** 44, 54
Bora Bora (French Polynesia) **4:** 43
borate minerals **1:** *45*
borax **1:** *45*; **8:** 27
bornite **1:** *36*; **8:** 15
boss **6:** 52, 53
brachiopods (Brachiopoda) **3:** *21–23*, 52, 53, 54, 55, 56
    recognising **3:** 21
Brazilian Shield **5:** 56
breccia **2:** *40–41*
Bristol Lake (California) **8:** 27
brittle stars **3:** 36
Broken Hill (Australia) **8:** *25*
brown coal *see* lignite
Bryce Canyon (Utah) **6:** 21; **7:** 5, 10, 13
Bushveld Complex (South Africa) **8:** 21
buttes **6:** 26, 27, 34

C

Cabot Fault (Canada) **6:** 50
cadmium **8:** 11
calcareous skeleton **3:** 6
calcite **1:** 18, 19, 23, *44*; **2:** 13
calderas **4:** *58–59*; **5:** 23; **6:** 52, 57
Caledonian Mountain Building Period **7:** 35
Caledonian Mountains **5:** 45; **7:** 30, 35, 37, 38
California Valley **5:** 39
Calymene **3:** 41, 54
calyx **3:** 34, 35
Cambrian, Cambrian Period **3:** 50*(chart)*; **7:** 18*(name)*, 21*(chart)*, 32*(map)*–33
    fossils **3:** 52
    life **7:** 33
    rocks **7:** 33
Canadian Rockies **5:** 40, 41 *see also* Rockies
Canadian Shield **5:** 56; **7:** 25, 27
Canyon del Colca (Peru) **5:** 37
canyons **6:** 26, 27
cap rocks **6:** 26–27, 30, 32, 53; **8:** 32
carbon **1:** 31
carbonate minerals **1:** *44–45*; **8:** 11, 53